Success guides

Leckie✕Leckie

D0495437

Intermediate 2
Physics

✕ John Taylor ✕

Contents

Mechanics and heat

Electricity and electronics

Waves and Optics

Radioactivity

Scalars and vectors, speed and velocity

Scalars and vectors

A **scalar** quantity has **magnitude** (size) only.

A **vector** quantity has **magnitude** (size) and also **direction**.

Distance, **d**, is a **scalar** and is added simply, without directions.

Displacement, **s**, is a **vector** and both the distance and direction from start to finish should be given.

Vectors are added 'head to tail' in diagrams. The **resultant** is drawn 'start to finish'.

e.g. A girl walks 10 m forward then comes back 7 m.
The distance travelled is 10 + 7 = 17 m.
The displacement is 10 + (–7) = 3 m forward.

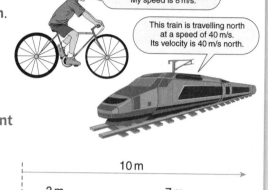

I travel 8 m every second. My speed is 8 m/s.

This train is travelling north at a speed of 40 m/s. Its velocity is 40 m/s north.

10 m

3 m   7 m

Calculating speed and velocity

The **speed** of an object is defined as the distance travelled in unit time (1 s).

Speed is a **scalar** quantity.

The **velocity** of an object is the speed in a given direction along a straight line. Velocity is defined as the displacement per unit time (1 s).

Velocity is a **vector** quantity.

Speed and velocity have the **units m/s**.

$$\text{speed} = \frac{\text{distance}}{\text{time}} \qquad v = \frac{d}{t}$$

$$\text{velocity} = \frac{\text{displacement}}{\text{time}} \qquad v = \frac{s}{t}$$

e.g. walking speed 2 m/s, jogging speed 5 m/s.

Equations can be put into a formula triangle:

Top Tip

You should also practise the formula triangle with other equations in this course.

Examples

1. A runner runs 10 000 m in 30 minutes.

   Calculate his speed.

   $$v = \frac{d}{t} = \frac{10\,000}{30 \times 60} = 5.6 \text{ m/s.}$$

2. A plane travels at 200 m/s. How far will it travel in 1 minute?

   $$d = v \times t = 200 \times 60 = 12\,000 \text{ m}$$

3. A rambler walks 2 km West then 3 km North in 2 hours.

   Find her (a) distance travelled (b) displacement (c) speed and (d) velocity.

3 km

2 km

   a) distance = 2 + 3 = 5 km.

   b) displacement (use Pythagoras and trig. or scale diagram)
      = 3.6 km @ 56.3° N of W.

   c) speed = distance / time $v = \dfrac{d}{t} = \dfrac{5}{2}$
      = 2.5 km/h.

   d) velocity = displacement / time $v = \dfrac{s}{t} =$
      $\dfrac{3.6}{2}$ = 1.8 km/h @ 56.3° N of W.

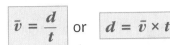

Measuring average speed

Average speed is the **total distance** travelled over the **total time** taken.

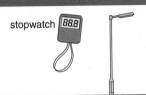

$$\bar{v} = \frac{d}{t} \quad \text{or} \quad d = \bar{v} \times t$$

($\bar{v}$ is pronounced v bar)

e.g. to **measure the average speed** of a cyclist on a road we would use a measuring tape and a stopwatch:

- Use the tape to measure a marked distance.
- Use the stopwatch to measure the time taken.
- Then we use the formula

$$\bar{v} = \frac{d}{t} \quad \text{or} \quad d = \bar{v} \times t \quad \text{to calculate the average speed.}$$

Top Tip
Think of situations where average and instantaneous speeds are different.

Measuring instantaneous speed – using a light gate

Instantaneous speed is the speed at a certain time.

A good estimate of instantaneous speed is obtained by using a **very small time interval**.

e.g. to **measure the speed** of a toy car:

A light gate (photocell and light beam) is attached to an electronic timer or computer timer.

A card is attached to the toy car. The length of card passes through the light beam.

- Use a **ruler** to measure the **length of card**.
- Use the **light gate** and **electronic timer** to measure the short **time** taken.

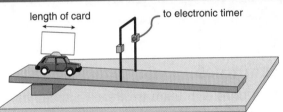

- Then we use the formula

$$v = \frac{d}{t} \quad \text{or} \quad d = v \times t$$

to **calculate** the instantaneous speed.

Quick Test

1. What should be given to fully describe a vector quantity?

2. A swimmer swims around a pool, length 20 m, breadth 10 m in 3 minutes. Calculate the distance, displacement, average speed and average velocity done by the swimmer.

3. Calculate the speed of a woman who runs 100 m in 12 s.

4. How long will it take for a man to run 120 m at 10 m/s?

5. How far will a car, travelling at 30 mph, travel in 30 minutes?

6. Give an example of where instantaneous speed and average speed are different.

Answers 1. Magnitude and direction **2.** 60 m, 0 m, 0.33 m/s, 0 m/s. **3.** 8.3 m/s **4.** 12 s. **5.** 15 miles **6.** On a journey, the instantaneous speed may change several times.

Acceleration

What is acceleration?

An object changing its velocity is accelerating. How much the velocity changes every second is a measure of the acceleration.

Acceleration, **a**, is the **change of velocity** in **unit time (1 s)**.

Acceleration is also defined as the **rate of change of velocity**.

My speed is increasing by 10 m/s each second. My acceleration is 10 m/s².

$$\text{acceleration} = \frac{\text{change in velocity}}{\text{time taken}} = \frac{\text{final velocity} - \text{initial velocity}}{\text{time}} \qquad a = \frac{v - u}{t}$$

Change in velocity is in m/s and time for change is in s; therefore acceleration has the **units m/s²**.

The acceleration equation can also be rearranged to give $\qquad v = u + at$

What is deceleration?

Since velocity is a vector, **acceleration** is also a **vector**. When the final velocity is less than the initial velocity, the acceleration will be negative.

A negative acceleration is a deceleration.

An acceleration of −5 m/s² is a deceleration of 5 m/s².

Examples

1. A bobsleigh team will reach a speed of 50 m/s from rest in 10 s.

   Calculate the acceleration.

   $$a = \frac{v - u}{t} = \frac{50 - 0}{10} = \frac{50}{10} = 5 \text{ m/s}^2$$

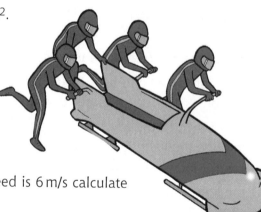

2. A car accelerates at 4 m/s² for 8 s. If its initial speed is 6 m/s calculate its final speed.

   $$a = \frac{v - u}{t} \quad \text{or} \quad v = u + at$$

   $$4 = \frac{v - 6}{8} \qquad\qquad = 6 + (4 \times 8)$$

   $$32 = v - 6 \qquad\qquad = 38 \text{ m/s}$$

   $$v = 38 \text{ m/s}$$

3. An animal slows from 12 m/s to rest in 4 s. What is its deceleration?

   $$a = \frac{v - u}{t} = \frac{0 - 12}{4} = \frac{-12}{4} = -3 \text{ m/s}^2$$

   therefore deceleration = 3 m/s².

Top Tip

Acceleration does not depend on velocity but change in velocity

Measuring average acceleration

Using **2 light gates and a stopwatch**.

A short length of card is attached to the vehicle to cut the light beam.

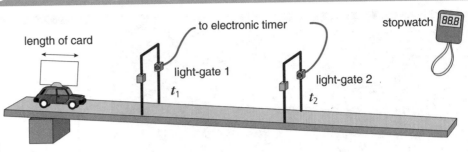

length of card

to electronic timer

stopwatch

light-gate 1
t_1

light-gate 2
t_2

- At light gate 1 we use the length of card and time to obtain an **initial velocity, u**.
- At light gate 2 we use the length of card and time to obtain a **final velocity, v**.
- The stopwatch is used to record the **time, t**, between the velocities.
- Then we can use the equation

$$a = \frac{v - u}{t}$$

to calculate the **average acceleration** between the light gates.

Measuring acceleration at a point

Here we use a **double card with single light gate** attached to a motion computer.

to motion computer

2   1

light-gate

The second card cuts the light beam quicker than the first.

The length of card needs to be measured and entered to the motion computer.

The motion computer records

    a. the **time** for the first card

    b. the **time** for the second card

    c. the **time** between the cards.

It can then calculate the **first** and **second velocities**, and the **acceleration**. Can you see how?

Top Tip
The motion computer needs to know the velocity and acceleration equations.

Quick Test

1. What is meant by the term acceleration?

2. Calculate the acceleration of a Fiat which increases its speed by 60 m/s in 20 s.

3. A VW is travelling at 10 m/s when it accelerates at 5 m/s for 3 s. What is its new speed?

4. A bus is travelling at 20 m/s when it decelerates at 2 m/s². How long does it take to stop?

5. A train slows from 35 m/s to 20 m/s in 5 s. What is its acceleration and deceleration?

Answers 1. Acceleration is the change in velocity in unit time. 2. 3 m/s² 3. 25 m/s 4. 10 s 5. −3 m/s² and 3 m/s²

Graphs of motion

We can use a velocity–time graph to show the journey of an object.

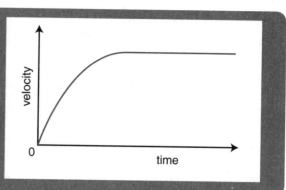

Velocity–time graphs

Describing motion from a velocity–time graph

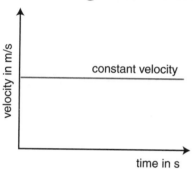

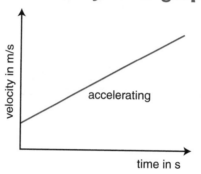

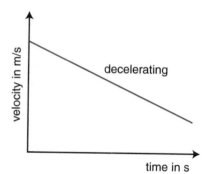

Horizontal line: object moving at **constant velocity**.

Straight line sloping upwards: constantly increasing velocity or **constant acceleration**.

Straight line sloping downwards: constantly decreasing velocity or **constant deceleration**.

Calculating displacement from a velocity–time graph

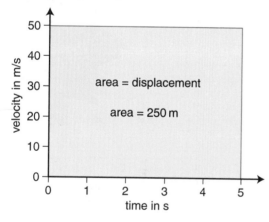

The **area** under a velocity–time graph gives the **displacement**, s, of an object.

s = area under a v/t graph

Top Tip

Remember if the velocity is negative, below the zero axis, the displacement will be negative for all of that part of the journey.

Calculating acceleration from a velocity–time graph

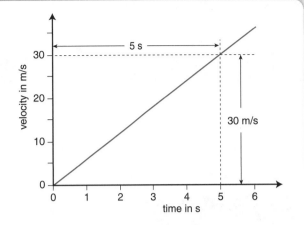

We can find the **acceleration** of an object by calculating the gradient of a velocity–time graph.

> a = gradient of a v/t graph

The acceleration of the object in this graph is:

$$\frac{30\,\text{m/s}}{5\,\text{s}} = 6\,\text{m/s}^2.$$

Example

A motorcyclist's journey is represented on the following graph.

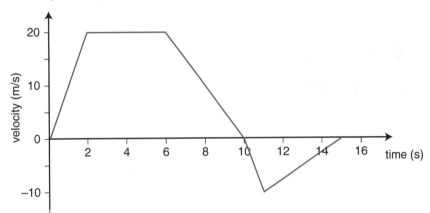

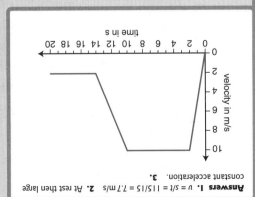

Top Tip

The largest acceleration is calculated from the line with the steepest gradient.

Describe the motions and calculate the accelerations and total displacement for this journey.

0–2 s: Constant acceleration of 20/2 = 10 m/s², displacement of $\frac{1}{2}$ 20 × 2 = 20 m.

2–6 s: Constant velocity at 20 m/s, a = 0 m/s², displacement of 20 × 4 = 80 m.

6–10 s: Constant acceleration of –20/4 = –5 m/s², displacement of $\frac{1}{2}$ 20 × 4 = 40 m.

10–11 s: Constant acceleration of –10/1 = –10 m/s², displacement of $\frac{1}{2}$ (–10 × 1) = –5 m.

11–15 s: Constant acceleration of –10/4 = –2.5 m/s², displacement of $\frac{1}{2}$ (–10 × 4) = –20 m.

0-15 s: Total displacement = (20 + 80 + 40) + (–5 – 20) = 140 – 25 = 115 m (distance travelled = 165 m).

Quick Test

1. In the example above, what is the average velocity of this journey?

2. In a velocity–time graph what does a horizontal line on the time axis followed by a straight line sloping steeply upwards show?

3. Draw a velocity–time graph for this journey:
   - A runner accelerates from rest to a velocity of 10 m/s in 2 s.
   - She then travels at this velocity for 8 seconds before decelerating to 2 m/s in 4 more seconds.
   - She continues to jog at this velocity for another 6 s.

Answers 1. $v = s/t = 115/15 = 7.7$ m/s **2.** At rest then large constant acceleration. **3.**

Forces

Effects of forces

A force, applied to an object, has the ability to change the
- **shape**   - **speed**   - **direction**

of an object.

Recognising forces

pushing off the blocks

pulling the grass roller

compressing the spring

twisting the bottle

lifting the bag

stretching the catapult

Measuring forces

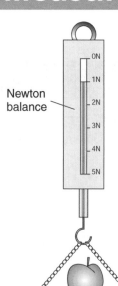

Newton balance

Force, F, is measured in newtons, N.

The size of a force is measured using a **newton balance**.

- A newton balance has a spring inside.
- A force applied to one end will cause the spring to extend or lengthen.
- The **greater the force** the **greater the extension** or increase in length.
- The marker moves on the scale in direct proportion.

1 N is about the weight of an average apple.

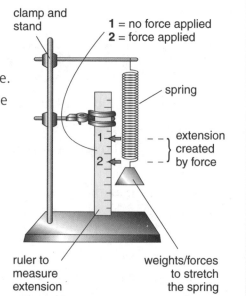

clamp and stand

1 = no force applied
2 = force applied

spring

extension created by force

ruler to measure extension

weights/forces to stretch the spring

Mass, gravity and weight

Mass

Mass is **the amount of matter** there is in an object.

Mass depends on the number and type of atoms.

Mass is a scalar – it has only size. No direction.

We measure mass in **kilograms (kg)**.

Gravitational field strength

On earth, **the weight of every 1 kg of mass is 10 N**.

The **weight per unit mass** is equal to the **gravitational field strength**.

$$g = \frac{W}{m}$$

PLANET	Mercury	Venus	Earth	Mars	Jupiter	Saturn	Uranus	Neptune
g (N/kg)	4	9	10	4	26	11	12	12

weight loss, but still the same mass!

The sun has $g = 270$ N/kg.

The acceleration due to gravity is numerically equal to the gravitational field strength.

On Earth, **acceleration, $a = 10$ m/s^2** and **gravitational field strength, $g = 10$ N/kg**.

On the Moon, **acceleration, $a = 1.6$ m/s^2** and **gravitational field strength, $g = 1.6$ N/kg**.

Weight

Weight is a force.

Weight is the Earth's **pull on an object**.

Weight acts **downwards**. Weight is a **vector**.

Weight depends on mass and the gravitational field strength.

$$W = mg$$

Examples

On Earth, **$g = 10$ N/kg** A bag of sugar with a mass of 1 kg weighs 10 N on Earth.

On the Moon, **$g = 1.6$ N/kg** The bag of sugar would have the same 1 kg mass but weigh only 1.6 N on the Moon.

This pile of rocks has been collected from the Moon. They contain 4 kg of matter.

On the Moon their mass is 4 kg and their weight is: **$W = mg = 4 \times 1.6 = 6.4$ N**

Back on Earth, the rocks have the same 4 kg mass, but their weight has increased: $W = mg = 4 \times 10 = 40$ N

Quick Test

1. What does a spring do to measure force?

2. What three things can a force change?

3. What is the unit of mass?

4. What is the weight, on Earth, of **a)** 100 g **b)** 500 g **c)** 1 kg **d)** 10 kg?

5. Why does the Moon not have as strong a pull on mass as the Earth has?

Answers 1. Extend **2.** Speed, shape, direction **3.** kg **4. a)** 1 N, **b)** 5 N, **c)** 10 N, **d)** 100 N **5.** The Moon has less gravitational field strength.

Newton's 1st and 2nd Laws

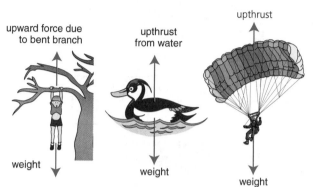

Balanced forces

Forces **opposing** each other may **cancel out**. Forces which cancel out are **balanced** forces.

balanced forces: no motion

Balanced forces are equal in size but opposite in direction.

Force is a vector quantity. Force has direction.

- **Balanced forces** are equivalent to **no force** at all.
- Balanced forces have no effect on motion.
  - An object **at rest will remain stationary**.
  - An object **in motion** will continue at the **same speed** in the **same direction**.

upward force due to bent branch

weight

upthrust from water

weight

upthrust

weight

Example

An aircraft is flying steadily.

Constant speed: size of driving force = air resistance

Constant altitude: size of lift force = weight

lift

driving force

drag

(or air resistance)

weight

Newton's first law of motion – NI

> **An object will REMAIN AT REST or will REMAIN AT CONSTANT VELOCITY unless acted on by an unbalanced force.**

Newton's first law applies when there are **no forces** or the **forces are balanced**. The velocity remains the same. Note: Constant velocity = constant speed in a straight line.

Question: What should you do to keep an object moving?
Answer: Do nothing! An object should just keep moving, see NI.

In space objects keep going without energy or rockets.
A force is only used when we want a CHANGE.

Normally we expect objects to stop. Newton says something must be doing the stopping. This is the **force** of **friction** between the object and the ground.

Seat belts and air bags

Newton I says an object should keep its speed. In a crash, if we are standing on a bus, or do not have a seat belt on, NI says we **will just keep going** – if the vehicle stops. We are **not** 'thrown forward'.

A **seat belt** applies a **force** in the **opposite direction** of motion which decelerates the person with the vehicle. A seat belt will have some 'give' so as not to cause injury.

Unbalanced forces

Forces applied to an object which do not cancel out are UNBALANCED.

- **Unbalanced forces** cause **acceleration**.
- The **difference** in the opposing forces must be calculated.

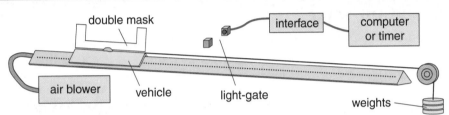

rocket pushed forward

stationary object made to move: unbalanced forces

fuel pushed back

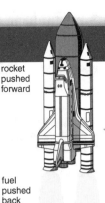

Top Tip

Balanced forces are equivalent to no force and cause no change in speed or direction. Unbalanced force causes acceleration.

Force and acceleration

An object whose motion (speed or direction) is changing is **accelerating**.

The weights are **applying a force** to the moving system (vehicle and weights).

double mask

interface

computer or timer

air blower   vehicle   light-gate

weights

Expt.1: The number of **weights** can be increased.   Expt.2: The vehicle can have different **mass**.

The **larger the force** the **greater the acceleration** – direct proportion.
The **larger the mass** the **smaller the acceleration** – inverse proportion.

Newton's second law of motion – NII

The **ACCELERATION** of an object varies **DIRECTLY** with the **UNBALANCED FORCE** and **INVERSELY** with its **MASS**.

$$a = F/m$$ $$F_{un} = ma$$ – NII

The **NEWTON** is **defined** as the **force** which causes a **mass of 1 kg** to **accelerate at 1 m/s²**.

Equivalence of acceleration due to gravity and gravitational field strength

Weight, **W**, is a force, **F**, which causes mass, **m**, to accelerate downwards.
The acceleration due to gravity, **g**, can be found from Newton's 2nd law: $$W = mg$$

acceleration due to gravity $$a = \frac{F}{m} = \frac{W}{m} = \frac{mg}{m} = g$$ gravitational field strength

Thus, **acceleration due to gravity** and **gravitational field strength** have the **same numerical values**:
e.g. on Mars, acceleration, $a = 3.8 \, m/s^2$ and gravitational field strength, $g = 3.8 \, N/kg$.

Quick Test

1. What effect do balanced forces have on the motion of an object?

2. What does the size of the acceleration of an object depend on?

3. Why does a car have a top speed?

4. If a 2 kg block is pulled with a force of 10 N and friction is 2 N,
   a) what is the size of the unbalanced force?
   b) what is the block's acceleration?

Answers 1. None 2. Unbalanced force, mass 3. Air resistance balances engine force 4. a) 8 N b) 4 m/s²

Vectors and resultant forces

Top Tip
Do not draw a vector line without an arrowhead!

Forces are vectors

Force is a vector quantity, it has both **magnitude** (size) and **direction**.

A force can be represented by an arrow. The length of the arrow indicates the magnitude of the force and the arrowhead shows the direction of the force.

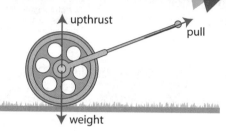

Resultant force

When two or more forces are acting on an object, they can be replaced by one single unbalanced force. The combined effect of the forces is called the **resultant** force.

Resultant of forces in a straight line

Draw a free body diagram to find the **resultant** or combined effect of forces in a straight line.
- Draw a diagram of the object.
- Use arrows to mark in all the forces.
- Check for forces not mentioned in the question, e.g. weight.
- Add forces that are in the same direction.
- Subtract forces in the opposite direction.

When giving your answer give the **size** and the **direction** of the resultant force.

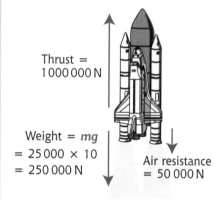

Thrust = 1 000 000 N

Weight = mg = 25 000 × 10 = 250 000 N

Air resistance = 50 000 N

Example

A rocket of mass 25 000 kg is accelerating with a thrust of 1 000 000 N while experiencing air resistance of 50 000 N. Find the resultant force on the rocket and hence its acceleration.

Resultant force
= total upward force – total downwards force
= 1 000 000 – 300 000
= 700 000 N upwards

Top Tip
Physics is F_{un} !

acceleration, $a = \dfrac{F_{un}}{m} = \dfrac{700\,000}{25\,000} = 28\,\text{m/s}^2$ upwards.

Example

A parachutist is descending towards the ground. At a certain point in time she experiences air resistance of 600 N upwards. If her mass is 70 kg determine her motion at that point.

Air resistance = 600 N

Weight = mg = 70 × 10 = 700 N

Resultant force
= total downwards force – total upwards force
= 700 – 600 = 100 N downwards

acceleration, $a = \dfrac{F_{un}}{m} = \dfrac{100}{70} = 1.4\,\text{m/s}^2$ downwards.

Resultant of forces at right angles

Two forces at right angles can be replaced with one **resultant force**.

When adding two forces at right angles, it is good to estimate the answer before you begin. The resultant force will not be as large as adding the two forces together as if they were pulling in the same direction, nor will the resultant be as small as subtracting the two forces as if they were in opposite directions. Also decide roughly which direction the resultant force will have.

Top Tip
Both magnitude and direction should be given when asked for a force.

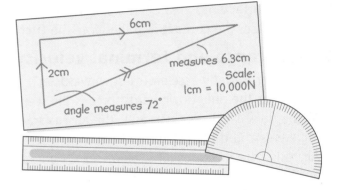

Example

Two tugs pull a ship off a pier. One pulls forward with a force of 60 000 N while the other pulls sideways with a force of 20 000 N. Calculate the resultant force on the ship.

Scale diagram method

- Choose a scale.
- Draw vectors 'head to tail'.
- Draw resultant 'start to finish'.
- Measure magnitude and direction.

Scale: 1 cm = 10 000 N

Resultant force = 6.3 × 10 000
                = 63 000 N @ 72° forward
                of the 20 000 N force.

6cm
2cm
measures 6.3cm
Scale:
1cm = 10,000N
angle measures 72°

Pythagoras and trigonometry method

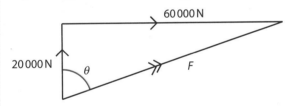

60 000 N

20 000 N   θ   F

$F = \sqrt{(20\,000^2 + 60\,000^2)} = 63\,245\,N$

$\tan\theta = opp / adj = 60\,000/20\,000 = 3$
$\theta = 71.6°$

This gives resultant force = 63 245 N @ 71.6° forward of the 20 000 N force.

Care should be taken with these calculated results. The tugs would not hold the stated force or angle and less significant figures are relevant.

Quick Test

1. What type of quantity is a force?

2. What is a resultant force?

3. A tug of war team pulls with a force of 400 N while the other team pulls with a 300 N force. What is the size of the combined force?

4. Two forces, both 8 N, pull at right angles to each other. What is the combined force?

5. Where is a resultant force drawn in a vector diagram?

Answers 1. A vector **2.** The combined effect of forces **3.** 100 N **4.** 11.3 N @ 45° from one force towards other. **5.** From 'start to finish'.

Friction and projectile motion

Friction

The **force of friction opposes the motion** of an object. Friction is a resistive force. When an object tries to move, or is in motion, friction is usually present. When one surface moves over another, friction exists. Rubbing our hands together or sliding a book along the bench lets us experience friction. Our shoes provide grip to let us walk.

Investigating the force of friction

The weight and the material can be changed.
Pull the shoe along at a **steady speed**.
The **pull** has the same strength as the **friction**.

A **rougher surface** has greater frictional force. A heavy weight increases the **contact** and therefore the **friction**.

weight
newton balance
shoe
carpet

Air resistance and terminal velocity

1 A skydiver **initially** accelerates downwards at $10\,m/s^2$ as the only downwards force is the weight.
2 As the diver's velocity increases, the **air resistance increases** and the acceleration is less.
3 Air resistance increases till it **balances** weight and a final constant velocity is reached at about $50\,m/s$.

air resistance
weight
weight

The **final**, constant velocity of a moving object is known as **TERMINAL VELOCITY**.

When the skydiver opens the parachute, the greater surface area means a lower terminal velocity will give the same air resistance to balance the weight for the diver to descend safely.

Air friction or resistance increases as
- the **velocity** increases
- the frontal **surface area** increases

Increasing friction

Increasing friction is useful to help an object speed up or slow down.

Dry **tyres** for racing cars have no tread to increase the contact area with the road. Aerofoils push cars down at speed for better **grip** in the corners. **Rough** tarmac is laid before traffic lights. **Clear roads** of wet leaves or spilt oil. Bike brakes work best in the **dry**. The parachute has a **large area** for more air to hit.

Reducing friction

Friction should be **reduced** where it opposes motion.

Streamlining of cars, cyclists, planes and bobsleighs reduces frontal area and saves fuel. Wheels, rollers and ball bearings are inventions that reduce friction and allow movement. **Roll not slide!**

air deflector

Hovercraft use a cushion of air to **reduce contact** with the ground. Wax skis to make them **smoother**. **Lubricate** machinery. This reduces the contact between the moving parts.

Newton's laws and friction

Newton's laws state that if we apply a force an object should accelerate, but sometimes we apply a force just to keep going. This is because our **push has been balanced by friction** and there is no unbalanced force. NI applies.

If we are accelerating, the accelerating force, F_{un}, is found: NII applies.

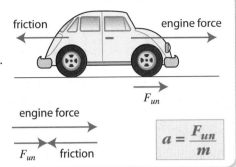

$$a = \frac{F_{un}}{m}$$

Projectile motion

Constant horizontal speed. $v = \dfrac{d}{t}$

Consider a space vehicle before re-entering our atmosphere.

It is travelling **horizontally at a constant speed**.

Gravity pulls on the space vehicle in a **vertically downwards** direction.

This creates an **acceleration downwards**. The vehicle follows a **projectile** path.

The **resultant speed** is a **combination** of the **horizontal** and the **vertical**.

Increasing vertical speed. $v = u + at$

Newton's thought experiment

Satellite motion extends the ideas of projectile motion. It was predicted by **Newton's Thought Experiment** over 300 years ago.

Newton thought if a cannon ball was fired off a very high mountain fast enough it would never reach the ground as Earth is curved. Instead it would remain in orbit and free-fall.

Today satellites are launched into orbit in space at great height. Earth's mountains are not high enough!
E.g. low orbit = 200 km, geo-stationary orbit = 36 000 km.

The satellites remain in orbit because of gravity.

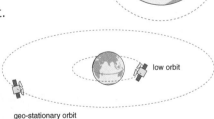

geo-stationary orbit

Quick Test

1. In what direction does friction act?

2. What does air friction depend on?

3. Name three ways of increasing friction.

4. Name three ways of decreasing friction.

5. A ball is kicked off a cliff with a horizontal speed of 5 m/s, what is its vertical speed and horizontal speed after 1 s?

Answers 1. Against the motion **2.** Roughness of surfaces, frontal area, velocity **3.** Increase contact area, roughen surfaces, dry brakes **4.** Lubrication, streamlining, rolling motion **5.** After 1 s, vertical speed = 10 m/s, horizontal speed = 5 m/s.

Newton pairs, momentum and collisions

Newton's 3rd law of motion – NIII

Newton's 2nd law tells us when a force is exerted on an object it will change its motion, but Newton also realised that the object also exerts an equal force back.

Forces occur in equal and opposite pairs. You push on a wall and the wall pushes you away. But how can a rocket in space 'push off'? The rocket exerts a thrust on its fuel, the fuel exerts an **equal but opposite** thrust on the rocket. (Thrust is another name for a force).

rocket pushed forward

hot gases pushed back

Newton's 3rd law:

> If A exerts a force on B, then B exerts an equal but opposite force on A.

NIII tells us **forces exist in pairs**. These are known as **Newton pairs**. 'Newton pairs' are acting on two different objects unlike Newton's 1st law where balanced forces act on one object.

Top Tip
You should now know Newton's three laws of motion.

There are many examples of Newton pairs:

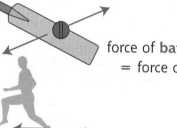

force of **bat on ball**
= force of **ball on bat**

force of **foot on ball**
= force of **ball on foot**

force of **boat on man**
= force of **man on boat**

force of **gun on bullet**
= force of **bullet on gun**

force of **car tyres on road**
= force of **road on car tyres**

force of **boy on seat**
= force of **seat on boy**

Momentum

A Newton pair exists when a capsule pushes off from its more massive parent ship.

Both experience the **same size of force**.
The product of **mass × velocity** is the same for each.
The capsule has a smaller mass × a larger velocity.
The ship has a larger mass × a smaller velocity.

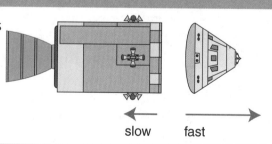

slow   fast

Momentum (p) is the product of mass and velocity

| momentum = mass × velocity | $p = mv$ |

Momentum is a .**vector** quantity.   Momentum has the **units kg m/s**

Collisions

When a car moving at 40 m/s collides into the back of a lorry moving at 10 m/s the resultant is not both moving at 50 m/s, i.e. not a simple addition. We say velocity is not conserved. In collisions, the resultant effect is dependent on the two factors **mass** and **velocity**. Motion is best described by measuring the product: mass × velocity, or **momentum**.

Conservation of momentum

In a collision, provided no external forces act, the total momentum before and after is the same.

before collision

The law of **conservation of momentum** applies:

after collision

total momentum **before** collision = **total** momentum **after** collision

This can be written as an equation: $m_1u_1 + m_2u_2 = m_1v_1 + m_2v_2$

m is the mass in kg   *u* is the velocities before   *v* is the velocities after

1 is the subscript for object 1   *2* is the subscript for object 2

Example

A lorry of mass 2000 kg, moving at 20 m/s, collides with a car of mass 1000 kg, which is stationary. What is the velocity of the car after the collision if the lorry now moves forward at 10 m/s?

Before

2000 kg	1000 kg
20 m/s	0 m/s

After

2000 kg	1000 kg
10 m/s	v m/s

total momentum before = total momentum after

$$m_1u_1 + m_2u_2 = m_1v_1 + m_2v_2$$
$$(2000 \times 20) + (1000 \times 0) = (2000 \times 10) + (1000v)$$
$$40\,000 + 0 = 20\,000 + 1000v$$
$$20\,000 = 1000v$$
$$v = 20 \text{ m/s forward}$$

During a collision the objects may stick together. In this case $v_1 = v_2$. The equation can remain the same.

Top Tip
Remember: Momentum is conserved, velocity is not.

Quick Test

1. Does a force exist on its own?

2. If a swimmer exerts a force on the water, what is the opposing force?

3. What is the momentum of an ice skater of mass 50 kg moving at 7 m/s?

4. An ice skater of mass 60 kg moving at 6 m/s collides and holds onto another of mass 30 kg who was at rest. What speed does the pair move off at?

Work and energy

Energy transformations

A car travelling steadily: **chemical potential** energy ⟶ **heat** energy

The car is accelerating: **chemical potential** energy ⟶ **heat + kinetic** energy

The car is climbing steadily: **chemical potential** energy ⟶ **heat + potential** energy

At the top, the car has gained **gravitational potential** energy

When a car brakes: **kinetic** energy ⟶ **heat** energy

Once energy changes to heat, it is often 'lost' to the surroundings.

Conservation of energy: Energy is never created or destroyed – just changed from one form to another.

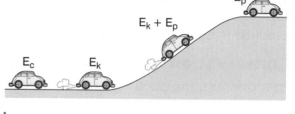

Work

Work is done when energy is **transferred** to an object or energy is **transformed**.

| work done = energy transferred |

Work and all forms of energy are **measured in joules**, J.

Work is done by appling a force through a distance. The object gains energy.

| work done = force × distance | $E_w = F \times d$ | $E_w = F \times d = 1000 \times 2 = 2000\,\text{J}.$ |

Work is a scaler, but the object moves in the direction of the applied force.

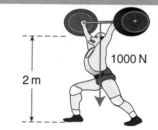

The weightlifter has done work.

Top Tip
When studying, do **work**! Take notes. **Force** the pen a large **distance**!

Gravitational potential energy

To LIFT an object through a height against gravity we need to DO WORK.

The **lifting force** required is **equal** in size to the object's **weight**. $\boxed{F = W = mg}$

The object has gained POTENTIAL ENERGY.

$$E_{P\,gain} = E_W$$
$$= F \times d$$
$$= mg \times b$$

$\boxed{E_P = mgb}$

where $g = 10\,\text{N/kg}$

A forklift truck has just done work. It has lifted a 50 kg bag 5 m onto a shelf.

| $E_P = mgb = 50 \times 10 \times 5 = 2500\,\text{J}.$ |

Whenever we **lift** a **mass** up through the **gravitational field** we do **work**. The object stores this as **gravitational potential energy**.

Kinetic energy

Kinetic energy is the **energy** of **moving** objects.

This air track vehicle is **accelerated** by the **energy** in the bands. **WORK is being done**. The vehicle gains **kinetic energy**.

The light gate is connected to the computer to measure the **velocity**.

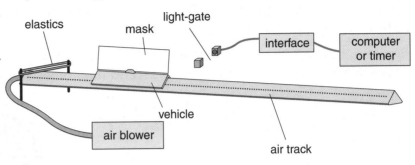

1 If the vehicle's mass is doubled, twice the energy (number of bands) is needed to get the same velocity. We can show $E_K \propto m$

2 To get the vehicle to double its velocity requires four times the energy (number of bands). We can show $E_K \propto v^2$ In fact $\boxed{E_K = \dfrac{1}{2}\, mv^2}$

- The **energy** depends on **mass**:
  A car and a lorry are going at the same speed. The lorry has more mass.
  It will take more work to stop. The more massive lorry has more kinetic energy.

- The **energy** depends on the **square of the velocity**:
  Two identical cars. One is going twice as fast as the other. $2^2 = 4$. It will have four times the energy. It will take four times as much work to stop. In a crash, four times as much energy to do damage!
  How much more energy will a vehicle need to become three times as fast?
  ... $3^2 = 9$ times!

A 1000 kg car is going at 30 m/s (70 mph). How much energy will be needed to stop it?

$$E_K = \frac{1}{2}\, mv^2 = \frac{1}{2}\, 1000\,(30^2) = 500 \times 900 = 450\,000\,J.$$

The kinetic energy of a vehicle is transformed to heat by the brakes. This **energy will be lost as heat to the surroundings**.

Stopping distance = thinking distance + braking distance

First the driver needs **thinking distance = speed × reaction time**. Then the work done by the brakes depends on the braking force and the braking distance. If a car doubles its speed, the driver will need at least four times more **braking distance** to convert the kinetic energy to heat.

Quick Test

1. What usually happens to 'lost' energy?

2. A girl pushes her bike for 300 m with a force of 70 N. How much work did she do?

3. A pupil weighing 500 N climbs the school stairs using 2500 J of energy. What height are the stairs?

4. A bag of mass 6 kg is lifted onto a table of height 0.8 m. What is the potential energy gained?

5. A 1 kg ball leaves the player's foot at 30 m/s. How much kinetic energy did the ball gain?

6. A stone of mass 0.5 kg is dropped from a height of 2 m. What is its initial potential energy, its kinetic energy and velocity before it hits the ground?

Answers 1. Lost energy heats the surroundings. **2.** 21000 J **3.** 5 m **4.** 48 J **5.** 450 J **6.** 10 J 10 J 6.3 m/s

Power and efficiency

Power

If we **time** how long it takes to do work or gain potential energy or transfer it to kinetic energy or heat we can calculate the power developed.

Power is the **work done every second** or the **rate of doing work**.
Power is the **energy transferred every second** (unit time) or the **rate of transferring energy**.

$$\text{power} = \frac{\text{work done}}{\text{time taken}}$$

$$\text{power} = \frac{\text{energy}}{\text{time taken}}$$

$$P = \frac{E}{t}$$ Power is measured in **watts (W)**.

Examples

1 A pupil of mass 50 kg climbs stairs of vertical height 7 m in a time of 9 s.

Lifting force = weight: $W = mg = 50 \times 10 = 500\,\text{N}$

Work done: $E_w = F \times d = 500 \times 7 = 3500\,\text{J}$
Potential energy gained: $E_p = mgh = 50 \times 10 \times 7 = 3500\,\text{J}$

Power: $P = E/t = 3500/9 = 389\,\text{W}$

2 A car of mass 800 kg, travelling at 20 m/s, is brought to rest in 40 s. What is the power of the brakes?

Work done = kinetic energy lost.

$$E_K = \frac{1}{2}mv^2 = \frac{1}{2} \times 800 \times 20^2 = 160\,000\,\text{J}.$$

$$\text{Power} = \frac{\text{work done}}{\text{time taken}} = \frac{160\,000}{40} = 4000\,\text{W or 4 kW.}$$

3 A crane lifts a load of bricks of mass 1200 kg onto a building of height 12 m.
The carrier itself has a mass of 300 kg.
What minimum power must the motor of the lift develop to lift the bricks in 15 s?

Work done = potential energy gained ($g = 10\,\text{N/kg}$)

$$E_p = mgh = 1500 \times 10 \times 12 = 180\,000\,\text{J}$$

$$\text{Power} = \frac{\text{work done}}{\text{time taken}} = \frac{180\,000}{15} = 12\,000\,\text{W or 12 kW.}$$

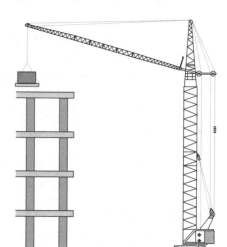

Note that **in real life** the power of the motor will have to be **greater** than this. There will be **energy lost as heat** due to **friction forces** as well as the kinetic energy required from the electrical energy of the motor. The total energy change is **electrical → kinetic → potential + heat**.

Efficiency

Energy is always **lost to the surroundings** in energy converters. The **waste energy is mainly heat**. Overall we say energy is being **degraded**. The energy cannot be put back.

We want to make all devices as efficient as possible.
Efficiency measures how much of the **total** we put **in** is kept as **useful output**.

$$\text{efficiency} = \frac{\text{useful output}}{\text{total input}}$$

This gives efficiency as a **fraction** of 1.

It is more common to give efficiency as a percentage. This will always be **less than 100%**.

$$\text{percentage efficiency} = \frac{\text{useful energy output}}{\text{total energy input}} \times 100$$

$$P = \frac{E}{t}$$

$$\text{percentage efficiency} = \frac{\text{useful power output}}{\text{total power input}} \times 100$$

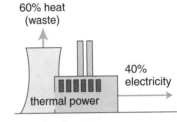

60% heat (waste)

40% electricity

thermal power

total efficiency = 40%

A thermal power station is usually no more than 40% efficient.

Examples

1 A microwave supplies 800 J of energy to food for every 1500 J of energy it takes in. What is the efficiency of this machine?

$$\text{percentage efficiency} = \frac{\text{Useful } E_o}{E_i} \times 100$$

$$= \frac{800}{1500} \times 100 = 53\%$$

2 In a 60 W filament lamp only 9 W is converted to light. The rest goes to heat. How efficient is this lamp?

$$\text{percentage efficiency} = \frac{\text{Useful } P_o}{P_i} \times 100$$

$$= \frac{9}{60} \times 100 = 15\%$$

Note: Efficiency applies to electrical as well as mechanical devices.

Top Tip
Efficiency is always less than 100%. We cannot get more out than we put in!

Quick Test

1. What is the basic unit of time?

2. A dog pulls a sledge for 1500 m using a force of 50 N. What work is done and what is the dog's average power if it takes the dog 10 minutes?

3. A 2 kW motor pulls a load of 3000 N for 8 m. How long does it take?

4. How efficient is a machine which takes in 24 000 J and produces 8000 J of useful energy?

5. A machine which is 70% efficient has an input power of 360 W. What is the output power?

6. If the output power from a 40% efficient machine is 2400 W, what is the input power?

Answers 1. 1 s 2. 75000 J, 125 W 3. 12 s 4. 33% 5. 252 W 6. 6000 W

Heat energy and change of temperature

Heat and temperature

Temperature, **T**, is a measure of how **hot** a substance is and is measured in **degrees celsius**, °C.
A thermometer will have 100 divisions between 0°C and 100°C but the divisions extend beyond this.

Heat, E_h, is a form of **energy** and is measured in **Joules**, **J**. Heat can be measured directly with a joulemeter or can be calculated from the power of a heater by using the equation

$$E_b = P \times t$$

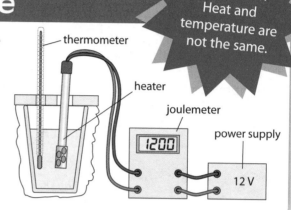

Storing heat

When heat energy is added to a material, it is stored in the material.

- **Heat and temperature are different**. Two different masses will store the same amount of heat but produce a different temperature rise.

- The same mass of **different materials need different quantities of heat energy** to be put in to change their temperature by the same amount. Aluminium has to be heated for longer than copper.

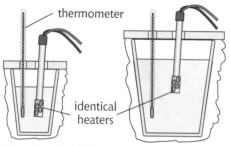

Same heat – different temperature rise!

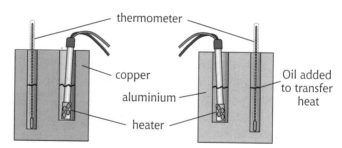

Same mass, same temperature rise, different heat required: Copper 386 J   Aluminium 902 J

Equal masses of three materials are all in the same hot water. They are at the same temperature. These **different materials store different amounts of energy**. When later put in three equal beakers of cold water they produce different temperature rises!

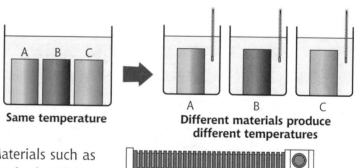

Same temperature

Different materials produce different temperatures

This effect is used in **storage heaters**. Materials such as brick or water rely on using **cheap off-peak electricity** to store heat in an **insulated container** of **water or bricks**. These materials store a lot of heat. This stored heat can then be **gradually released** into a home during the day.

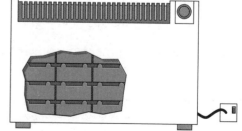

Specific heat capacity

The amount of **heat energy** required **to raise the temperature** of a substance depends on three factors: **temperature change**, **mass** and **material**.

The greater the temperature change we desire, the more energy will **be required**. A greater mass of material will require a greater amount of heat for the same temperature rise. Different materials require different quantities of energy to raise their temperature by one degree.

The same amount of energy used to heat up a substance will **be given out** when the substance cools.

The amount of **heat energy** required to raise the temperature of a substance:

- **varies with** the change in **temperature** required ($E \propto \Delta T$)
- **varies with** the **mass** being heated ($E \propto m$)
- **varies with** the **specific heat capacity** of the material being heated ($E \propto c$)

The amount of heat energy depends on all three factors: $\boxed{E = cm\Delta T}$

$$c = \frac{E}{m\Delta T} \qquad m = \frac{E}{c\Delta T} \qquad \Delta T = \frac{E}{cm}$$

Specific heat capacity

Specific heat capacity, c, is the amount of energy required to change the temperature of 1 kg of a substance by one degree celsius. This is also the energy 1 kg of a substance can **store** for each degree.

Water has a very high specific heat capacity, $c = 4180\,\text{J/kg}°\text{C}$.
It takes a lot of heat to make water hot. Water can store a lot of heat.

Example
The energy required to raise the temperature of 3 kg of water from 20 °C to 50 °C is:

$E = c\,m\,\Delta T = 4180 \times 3 \times 30 = 376\,200\,\text{J}$.

Measuring specific heat capacity

This block of steel has holes drilled to take the heater and the thermometer. Oil conducts the heat. To measure the specific heat capacity

- We measure the **energy** supplied
- the **mass** of the block and the **temperature** rise
- then **calculate** using $c = \frac{E}{m\Delta T}$

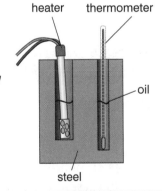

heater   thermometer

oil

steel

Quick Test

1. If you heat 1 kg of water in a kettle from room temperature of 20 °C to boiling point of 100 °C, how much energy does this take?

2. How long would this kettle take to boil if its power is 2200 W?

3. In practice, this kettle took 3 minutes. Why?

4. What is the unit of specific heat capacity?

5. A kettle gives out 167 200 J of heat energy when water at 100 °C cools to 20 °C. How much water is in the kettle?

Answers 1. $E = cm \Delta T = 4180 \times 1 \times 80 = 334\,400\,\text{J}$ **2.** $t = E/P = 334\,400 / 2200 = 152\,\text{s}$ **3.** Heat was lost to the surroundings as well.   **4.** J / kg°C   **5.** $m = E / c \Delta T = 167\,200 / 4180 \times 80 = 0.5\,\text{kg}$

25

Heat energy and change of state

Change of state

The three main **states of matter** are **solid**, **liquid** and **gas**.

Solid state: Atoms are **fixed** in a **structure** but have energy to **vibrate**.
Liquid state: Atoms have more energy and are **free to tumble**.
Gas state: Atoms have enough energy to **break free** and **stay** further **apart**.

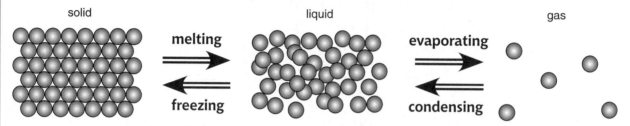

When a **solid changes to a liquid** this is called **melting** and energy is put **in**.
When a **liquid changes to a gas** this is called **evaporation** and energy is put **in**.
When a **gas changes to a liquid** this is called **condensation** and energy is given **out**.
When a **liquid changes to a solid** this is called **freezing** and energy is given **out**.

Energy has to be **gained or lost** by a substance to **change its state**. Time is taken for a substance to change state. During this time there is <u>**NO change in temperature**</u>.

A **picnic box cool pack** is frozen in a fridge. When placed beside the food it **takes heat energy from the food** to melt, keeping the food cool. When we **step out of the shower**, water on our skin **evaporates, taking heat energy** from our bodies, making us cool. In these examples, a change of state causes a change in temperature!

Top Tip
When ice is melting, the ice is 0°C and the water is 0°C.

Cooling curves

When a substance is at **higher temperature than its surroundings**, energy is given **out**.

When the temperature drops, energy is being given out. Note: The temperature drops quickest at the start when there is a **large temperature difference with the surroundings**. The temperature finally stops dropping when it is at the same temperature as the surroundings (room temperature).

The **temperature stays the same during a change of state**. The temperature stays the same, but energy is still being given out! The temperature stays the same until all the atoms have changed state. Each atom loses some energy.

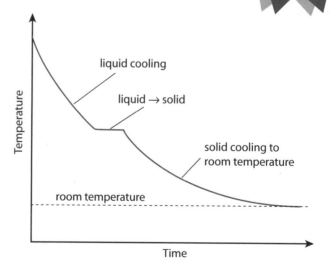

Latent heat capacity

The amount of **heat energy** required **to change the state** of a substance depends on two factors: **mass** and **material**.

A greater mass of material will require a greater amount of heat to change its state.

Different materials require different quantities of energy to change their states.

The amount of **heat energy** required to **change the state** of a substance:

- **varies with** the **mass** being heated ($E \, \alpha \, m$)
- **varies with** the **specific LATENT heat** of the material being heated ($E \, \alpha \, l$)

The amount of heat energy depends on these two factors: $\boxed{E = ml}$

$$\boxed{m = \frac{E}{l}} \qquad \boxed{l = \frac{E}{m}}$$

Top Tip

Latent means hidden. (We do not see a change in temperature during a change of state.)

SPECIFIC LATENT HEAT

The **specific latent heat**, l, is the amount of **heat energy**, E, to change the state of **1 kg of mass, m,** of a substance.

LATENT HEAT OF FUSION

This is the amount of energy per kg taken in or released to change **between a solid and a liquid state**.

e.g. Specific latent heat of fusion of ice, $l_f = 3.34 \times 10^5$ J/kg.

Note: The amount of energy **taken in** for **melting** is the same as will be **given out** when **freezing**.

LATENT HEAT OF VAPOURISATION

This is the amount of energy per kg taken in or released to change **between a liquid state and a gas**.

e.g. Specific latent heat of vaporisation of water, $l_v = 2.26 \times 10^6$ J/kg.

Note: The amount of energy **taken in** for **evaporating** is the same as will be **given out** when **condensing**.

Energy changes

From conservation of energy:

Electrical energy used = Heat energy gained. $\boxed{Itv = cm\Delta T}$ or $\boxed{Itv = ml}$

e.g. A kettle with no thermostat is boiling. The power of the kettle is known.
The time to evaporate a certain mass of water is noted.

$P = 2200$ W

$t = 10$ minutes $= 600$ s

$m = 0.6$ kg

$Pt = ml$

$2200 \times 600 = 0.6 \times l$

$l_v = 2.2 \times 10^6$ J/kg

Quick Test

1. How much energy is required to melt 0.5 kg of ice?

2. How much energy and time does a 2200w kettle required to evaporate 0.5 kg of water at 100 °C?

3. What are the units of specific latent heat?

Answers 1. $E = ml = 0.5 \times 3.34 \times 10^5$ **2.** $E = ml = 0.5 \times 2.26 \times 10^6 = 1.13 \times 10^6$ J, $t = E/P = 1.13 \times 10^6 / 2200 = 514$ s, ~ 8.6 minutes **3.** J/kg.

Key facts and questions

Summary questions and answers. Fuller answers are obtained by referring back to the revision notes.

Kinematics pp 4–9

1. How do you measure average speed?
2. What is the average speed when 10 km are covered in 2 hours?
3. How do you measure instantaneous speed?
4. When might average speed and instantaneous speed be different?
5. What is meant by scalar and vector quantities?
6. What is the difference between distance and displacement?
7. What is meant by speed, velocity and acceleration?
8. What is the motion when a velocity-time graph shows a straight line moving up? Moving down?
9. How is displacement found from a velocity-time graph?
10. How is acceleration found from a velocity-time graph?
11. What is the acceleration of an object whose initial velocity is 2 m/s, final velocity is 10 m/s when it takes 4 s to change velocity?

Answers

1. Use a measuring tape to measure a marked distance. Use a stopwatch to measure the time taken. Then calculate the average speed.
$$\bar{v} = \frac{d}{t} \quad \text{or} \quad \bar{v} = \frac{d}{t}$$
2. $\bar{v} = d/t = 10000 / (2 \times 60 \times 60) = 1.4$ m/s.
3. A good estimate of instantane 1 time interval. $v = d/t$. (See p 5 for light gate method.)
4. On a journey, the instantaneous speed may change several times.
5. A scalar quantity has magnitude (size) only. A vector quantity has magnitude (size) and also direction.
6. Distance is the total distance gone, without regard for direction. Displacement is the distance gone in a straight line from start to finish.
7. The speed of an object is defined as the distance travelled in unit time (1 s). Velocity is defined as the displacement per unit time (1 s). Acceleration is the change of velocity in unit time (1 s).
8. Constant acceleration, constant deceleration.
9. Displacement, s = area under a v/t graph.
10. Acceleration, a = gradient of a v/t graph.
11. $a = (v-u)/t = (10-2)/4 = 2$ m/s^2
$$a = \frac{v-u}{t}$$

Dynamics pp 10–17

1. What are balanced forces?
2. Describe Newton's first law of motion.
3. Describe Newton's second law of motion.
4. What is meant by the resultant of a number of forces?
5. What force is needed to accelerate 2 kg at 3 m/s^2 if friction is 4 N?
6. How do you find the resultant of two forces at right angles?
7. Show the equivalence of a and g
8. Explain projectile motion.

Answers

1. Balanced forces are equal in size but opposite in direction (= no force).
2. An object will remain at rest or will remain at constant velocity unless acted on by an unbalanced force.
3. The acceleration of an object varies directly with the unbalanced force and inversely with its mass. $F_{un} = ma$
4. When two or more forces are acting on an object, they can be replaced by one single unbalanced force. The combined effect of the forces is the resultant force.
5. $F_{un} = ma = 2 \times 3 = 6$N. $F = 6 + 4 = 10$N.
6. Scale diagram or trig. Size and direction (p 15).
7. $a = \frac{F}{m} = \frac{W}{m} = \frac{mg}{m} = g$
8. Constant horizontal velocity plus constant vertical acceleration due to gravity.

Momentum and energy pp 18–23

1. Describe Newton's third law of motion.
2. Give an example of a Newton pair.
3. What is momentum?
4. What is the law of conservation of linear momentum?
5. What is work done?
6. What is the work done when a 100N force is used to pull a sledge 50 m?
7. What is the relation between power and work?
8. What is the equation for potential energy?
9. What is the equation for kinetic energy?
10. What are the equations for efficiency?

Answers

1. 'If A exerts a force on B, then B exerts an equal but opposite force on A.'
2. Force of rocket on fuel = force of fuel gases = force of fuel gases on rocket. (Other examples on p 18.)
3. Momentum is the product of mass and velocity. Momentum is a vector quantity. $p = mv$
4. In a collision, provided no external forces act, the total momentum before and after is the same. **total** momentum before = **total** momentum after
$$m_1u_1 + m_2u_2 = m_1v_1 + m_2v_2$$
5. Work done is a measure of the energy transferred.
work done = force x distance $E_w = F_d$
6. $E_w = F_d = 100 \times 50 = 5000$J
7. Power is the work done every second or the rate of doing work. $P = \frac{E}{t}$
8. $E_p = mgh$
9. $E_k = \frac{1}{2}mv^2$
10. Percentage Efficiency = $\frac{\text{Useful Energy Output}}{\text{Total Energy Input}} \times 100$
Percentage Efficiency = $\frac{\text{Useful Power Output}}{\text{Total Power Input}} \times 100$

Heat pp 24–27

1. State what different materials require to change their temperature by one degree.
2. What is the relation between heat energy and temperature change?
3. What happens to heat energy when a substance changes state?
4. What happens to temperature when a substance changes state?
5. What is the relation between heat energy and the specific latent heat?
6. What are the names for specific latent heat when changing state between
   a) solid and liquid and **b)** liquid and gas?

Answers

1. The same mass of different materials needs different quantities of heat energy to change their temperature by one degree.
2. $E = cm\Delta T$
3. Energy has to be gained or lost by a substance to change its state.
4. A change of state does NOT involve a change in temperature.
5. $E = ml$
6. **(a)** Specific latent heat of fusion. **(b)** Specific latent heat of vaporisation.

Static electricity, electric current

Charges

The Atom: the atom

nucleus
protons (+)
neutrons (0)

orbiting
electrons (–)

In a **neutral** atom:
the number of **protons** = the number of **electrons**.

Static electricity

An **electron** from the outer orbit of an atom can be stripped off.

Two insulators rubbing together can become electrically charged by the **transfer of electrons** (negative charges) between them.

The object that **gains electrons** is said to be **negatively charged**.

The object that **loses electrons** is said to be **positively charged**.

Like charges repel
unlike charge attract

uncharged plastic rod

rod gains electrons and becomes negatively charged

uncharged cloth

cloth loses electrons and becomes positively charged

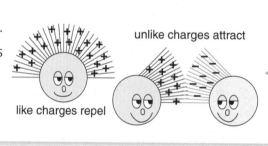

unlike charges attract

like charges repel

Top Tip
Protons are stuck in the nucleus of atoms.

Conductors and insulators

Electrons are **free to move** in a **conductor**.

In an **insulator** the **electrons are all bound** in the atom.

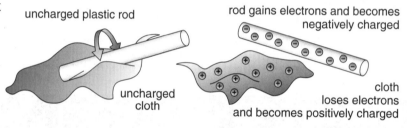

Good conductors are metals (e.g. gold, silver, copper and aluminium) and carbon.

Insulators are usually non-metal (e.g. pvc, polythene, wood, rubber and paper).

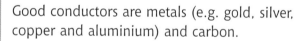

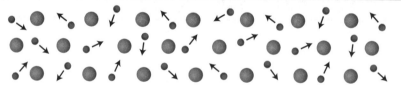

Baco Foil

Electric current

When charges (e.g. electrons) flow we have made an electric current.

Current is the **rate at which charge flows**.
Current is the **amount of charge** passing in **unit time (1 s)**.

current = $\dfrac{\text{charge}}{\text{time}}$ charge = current × time

Current (I) is measured in **amperes (A)**.
Charge (Q) is measured in **coulombs (C)**
Time (t) is measured in **seconds (s)**

$$I = \frac{Q}{t} \qquad Q = It$$

e.g. 6 C passes a point in 2 minutes. What is the value of the current?

$$I = \frac{Q}{t} = \frac{6}{2 \times 60} = \frac{6}{120} = 0.05\text{A}$$

Measuring Current

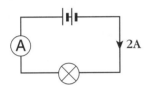

An **ammeter** is placed **in line** (in series) with the circuit.

$I = 2$ A. This means 2 C of charge flows through the bulb every 1 s.

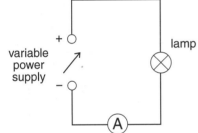

variable power supply

lamp

light meter

In this circuit, as the power supply is increased, the **current** increases and so does the brightness of the bulb.

Top Tip
Electrons are important for both static electricity and electric current.

Quick Test

1. What type of charge is on **a)** a proton, **b)** a neutron and **c)** an electron?

2. What type of charge flows in electric circuits?

3. A proton and electron are close together. Will they attract or repel?

4. Why are electrical wires made of copper and covered in plastic?

5. A circuit current is 0.5A. How much charge passes in 3 minutes?

Answers 1. a) positive, **b)** neutral, **c)** negative   **2.** negative electrons   **3.** attract   **4.** copper is a conductor, plastic is an insulator   **5.** Q = It = 0.5 × (3 × 60) = 90 C.

Voltage and energy

Voltage and potential difference

The voltage of a supply is a measure of the energy given to the charges in a circuit.

The **voltage** (or potential difference) across a **lamp** is a measure of the **energy** given **out** by **charges** as they go through the lamp.

Voltage (V) or **p.d.** is measured in **volts (V)**.

A voltage of 1 V means 1 J of electrical energy is changing into other forms every time 1 C of charge passes through.

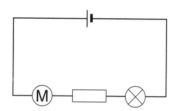

Top Tip

This equation may help you understand voltage

$$V = \frac{E}{Q}$$

but it is not required for the Intermediate 2 exams.

In this circuit:

- the charges have gained energy from the cell
- the bulb changes some of the electrical energy into light
- the resistor changes some of the electrical energy into heat
- the motor changes some of the electrical energy into kinetic energy.

Measuring Voltage

A **voltmeter** is placed **across** (in parallel with) the component being measured.

e.g. voltages from a battery:

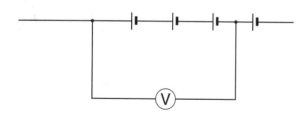

Number of cells	Voltage (V)
1	1.5
2	3.0
3	4.5
4	6.0

Top Tip

Review the meanings of current and voltage.

A voltage reading of 4.5 V here means 4.5 J of energy are being supplied for each 1 C of charge passing through the battery.

Voltage and brightness

In this circuit the brightness of the lamp is a measure of the **energy** supplied.

In this circuit, as the power supply is increased, the **voltage** or **potential difference** across the lamp increases and so does the brightness of the bulb.

We have now seen, both **voltage** and **current** have an effect on the **energy** delivered by the circuit.

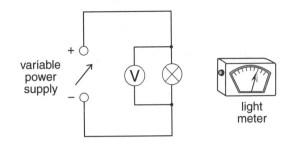
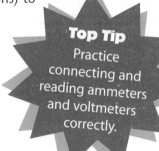

Comparing voltage and current

Voltage applied to a circuit provides **energy** and causes charges (electrons) to flow and the **rate of flow of charge** is called the **electric current**.

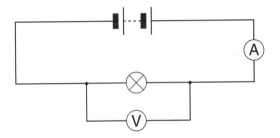

Top Tip
Practice connecting and reading ammeters and voltmeters correctly.

Circuit symbols

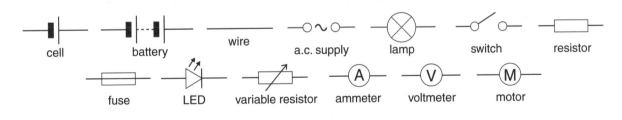

cell   battery   wire   a.c. supply   lamp   switch   resistor

fuse   LED   variable resistor   ammeter   voltmeter   motor

Quick Test

1. What is another name for potential difference?

2. What do charges gain from a cell?

3. When applied voltage increases, does current stay the same, increase or decrease?

4. The voltage on a battery is a measure of the energy given to the charges. True or false?

5. What is the symbol for a fuse?

Answers 1. voltage **2.** energy **3.** increase **4.** true **5.** line through rectangle.

Resistance and Ohm's Law

Resistance changes current

Materials oppose charges passing through them. This is **resistance**, an **opposition to current**.

Increasing the resistance of a circuit **decreases the current** in that circuit.

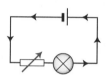
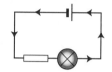

| With no resistors in the circuit, there will be a large current. | With a resistor in the circuit, there will be a smaller current. | Altering the value of this variable resistor changes the brightness of the bulb. |

Resistance (R) is measured in **ohms (Ω)**.

Electrical components

Electrical components in a circuit also resist current. They have resistance.

The resistance of a component can be **measured** using an **ohmmeter**.

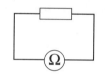

If, when a p.d. of 1 V is applied across a component, there is a current of 1 A; the component has a resistance of 1 Ω.

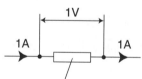

the resistance of this component is 1Ω

Resistance can be **calculated** using

resistance = voltage / current

$$R = \frac{V}{I}$$

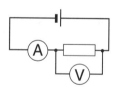

Example:

A current of 3 A is created in a circuit when a p.d. of 12 V is applied across a motor.

What is the resistance of this motor?

$$R = \frac{V}{I} = \frac{12}{3} = 4\,\Omega.$$

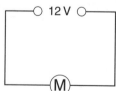

Ohm's Law

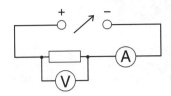

A range of p.d.s is applied across a conductor and the **corresponding** currents measured.

Voltage (V)	Current (A)

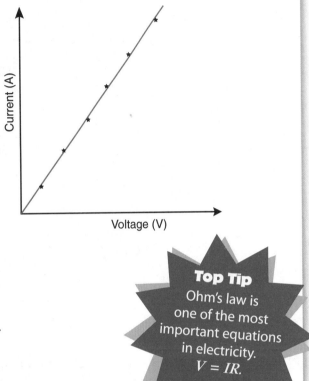

Assuming the temperature of the conductor does not change, the graph shows **a straight line passing through the origin**.

The shape of the graph shows **the current in a conductor is directly proportional to the voltage applied.**

This conclusion is known as Ohm's law.

The ratio $\dfrac{V}{I}$ remains constant for different currents.

$$R = \frac{V}{I} \qquad V = IR \qquad \text{Ohm's Law}$$

Top Tip

Ohm's law is one of the most important equations in electricity. $V = IR$.

Example:

If there is a current of 0.5 A with a 1 V supply, what will be the currents at 2 V, 3 V, 4 V, 5 V?

As current increases proportionally with voltage, we would expect 1.0 A, 1.5 A, 2.0 A and 2.5 A

Quick Test

1. When resistance decreases, what does current do?

2. What meter can measure resistance?

3. What voltage is required to create a current of 1 A in a 3 Ω resistor?

4. What assumption is made during the Ohm's law experiment?

5. A circuit resistance of 24 Ω is changed to 12 Ω. What will happen to the current?

6. What current is drawn from the mains voltage of 230 V by a component of resistance 1 kΩ? What current would be drawn if the component is used abroad with a voltage of 115 V?

Series and parallel, potential dividers

Series circuits

Series circuits have all the components in a **row** or **loop**. There are no branches.

There is only **one path** for the flow of charge.

A series circuit is turned on or off by a single switch or break anywhere in the circuit.

Current

The **current** is the **same** at all points of a series circuit.

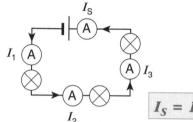

$$I_S = I_1 = I_2 = I_3$$

Voltage

The **sum** of the **voltages** across all the components in series is equal to the supply voltage.

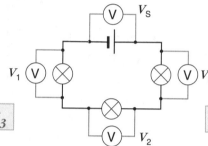

$$V_S = V_1 + V_2 + V_3$$

(s = supply)

Resistance

If we join components **in series** we **increase** the **resistance** of the circuit. The **current will decrease**.

The **total resistance** in series is equal to the **sum** of the individual resistances.

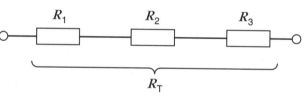

$$R_T = R_1 + R_2 + R_3$$

Potential dividers

Potential divider circuits use 2 or more resistors or a potentiometer to provide a part of a supply voltage, V_S.

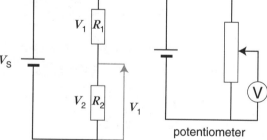

potentiometer

The voltage divides in the ratio of the resistors:

$$\frac{V_1}{V_2} = \frac{R_1}{R_2}$$

Now $I_S = I_1 = I_2$

So $\dfrac{V_S}{R_T} = \dfrac{V_1}{R_1} = \dfrac{V_2}{R_2}$

Giving alternative equations: $V_2 = \dfrac{R_2}{R_T} . V_S$ or $V_2 = \dfrac{R_2}{R_1 + R_2} . V_S$

[$R_T = R_{Total}$ and $V_S = V_{supply}$]

Parallel circuits

Parallel circuits have **branches** and **junctions**. There is **more than one path** for the charges to follow. A break in one branch has no effect on the other branches. Switches can turn off all or part of the circuit.

Current

The **sum** of the **currents** in parallel branches is equal to the current drawn from the supply.

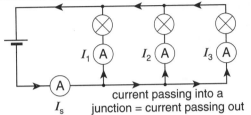

circuit has branches and more than one path to follow

current passing into a junction = current passing out

$$I_S = I_1 + I_2 + I_3$$

Voltage

The **voltages** across components in parallel **are the same** and equal to their supply.

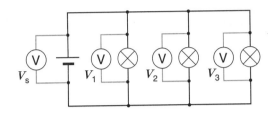

$$V_S = V_1 = V_2 = V_3$$ (s = supply)

Take care with parallel circuits. Adding too many appliances to one socket is dangerous as too large a current could be drawn from the supply. Overheating may occur.

Resistance

If we join components in **parallel** we **decrease the resistance** of the circuit. The **current will increase**.

The total resistance in parallel is calculated using a less than straightforward formula!

$$\frac{1}{R_T} = \frac{1}{R_1} + \frac{1}{R_2} + \frac{1}{R_3}$$ (For two resistors in parallel: $R_T = \frac{\text{product}}{\text{sum}}$)

Resistor combinations

Calculate a **combination circuit** by combining the **parallel resistances first**, then **add the series resistances** to find the total.

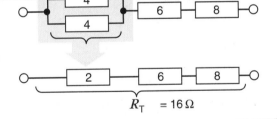

$R_T = 16\,\Omega$

Top Tip
Two identical resistors in parallel have half the resistance of one!

Quick Test

1. What type of circuit has all the components in a row?

2. In which type of circuit can a part be turned off?

3. If a 6 V battery is placed across three identical bulbs in series, what is the voltage across the middle bulb?

4. If three parallel branches each have 3 V across them, what is the voltage of the supply?

5. Two 2 Ω resistors in parallel follow a 2 Ω resistor. What is the total value?

Answers 1. Series **2.** Parallel **3.** 2V **4.** 3V **5.** $1 + 2 = 3\,\Omega$.

Power and energy

Power and energy

A supply **voltage** provides **energy to charges**. These charges move round the circuit as an electric current. When there is an electrical current in a component, there is an **energy transformation**.

In a **lamp electrical energy** is **transformed** into **heat** and **light** energy.
In a filament lamp this takes place in a resistance wire (more heat than light).
In the discharge lamp this takes place in the gas (less heat given off).
The **energy transformation** in an **electrical heater** occurs in the **resistance wire**, the element.

Power

Power is the **rate** at which **energy is transformed**.

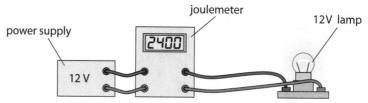

A 24 W lamp uses 2400 J in 100 s => 24 J/s
A 36 W lamp uses 3600 J in 100 s => 36 J/s

Power P is the amount of **energy E** transformed in **unit time (1 s)**.

$$\text{Power} = \frac{\text{Energy}}{\text{Time}} \qquad P = \frac{E}{t}$$

Energy (E) is measured in **joules (J)**.
Time (t) is measured in **seconds (s)**.
Power (P) is measured in **watts (W)**.

Examples

1) If a lamp has a power rating of 60 W, it changes 60 J of electrical energy into heat and light every 1 s.
2) If a fire has a power rating of 2 kW, it changes 2000 J of electrical energy into heat and light every 1 s.
3) If a 12 V lamp uses 14 400 J of energy in 5 minutes, what is its power?

$$P = \frac{E}{t} = \frac{14\,400}{5 \times 60} = 48\,\text{W}$$

Top Tip
Energy is the key to electricity. The ideas of voltages, power and circuits are all connected to energy.

Energy

How many joules of electrical energy have been transformed?

$$\text{energy} = \text{power} \times \text{time} \qquad E = P \times t$$

How much electrical energy is converted when a 150 W TV is on for 6 hours?

$$E = Pt = 150 \times (6 \times 60 \times 60) = 150 \times 21\,600 = 3\,240\,000\,\text{J}$$

That's over 3 million!

These equations for Power and Energy are also found in the other physics topics.

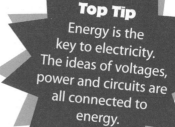

Top Tip
Learn the power ratings of appliances around your home. Understanding the power ratings is vital.

Power, voltage and current

Power also depends on the **voltage** across and the **current** in a component.
If 1 V across a component creates a current of 1 A, then the power is 1 W.

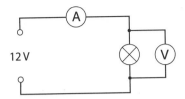

power = current × voltage

$$P = IV$$

A 12 V, **12 W** lamp will draw a current of **1 A** from a 12 V supply.
A 12 V, **24 W** lamp will draw a current of **2 A** from a 12 V supply.
A 12 V, **36 W** lamp will draw a current of **3 A** from a 12 V supply.
e.g. A 230 V kettle draws a current of 10 A from the mains.

$$P = IV = 10 \times 230 = 2300\,W$$

Top Tip
Power equations
$$I = \frac{P}{V}$$
can be used to select a fuse value.

Equivalent power equations

Start with the equation $P = IV$ and substitute in $V = IR$ or $I = V/R$ from **Ohm's law** to give further power equations:

$$P = IV = I(IR) = I^2R$$

$$P = IV = \left(\frac{V}{R}\right)V = \frac{V^2}{R}$$

There are now four equations for **electrical power**:

$$P = \frac{E}{t} \qquad P = IV \qquad P = I^2R \qquad P = \frac{V^2}{R}$$

Top Tip
When reading a question, make a list of the quantities given, then choose the equation.

Quick Test

1. A drill uses 90 000 J of energy in 3 minutes. Calculate its power.
2. A 1.4 kW vacuum cleaner is used for 30 minutes. How much energy has it used?
3. A 3 V bulb draws 250 mA from a battery. What is its power? How much energy is used in 5 minutes?
4. A heater draws a current of 6 A through its 40 Ω element. What is its power rating?
5. Calculate the resistance of the filament of a 60 W, 230 V lamp.

Answers 1. 500 W 2. 2 520 000 J 3. 0.75 W, 225 J 4. 1440 W 5. 882 Ω

AC/DC

Electrical supply

There are **two** types of power supply.

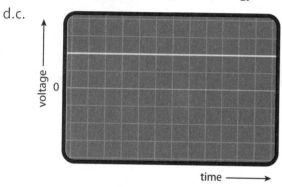

d.c.

cell   battery   power supply

a.c.

power supply   signal generator

The CRO (**cathode ray oscilloscope**) shows the **voltage** of these power supplies.

Voltage can be said to give 'push' to the charges.

There are two different ways the energy is supplied to the charges.

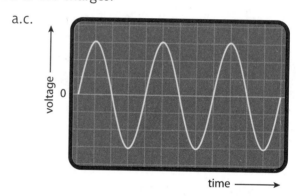

d.c.

voltage

0

time

a.c.

voltage

0

time

direct voltage => direct current

alternating voltage => alternating current

For d.c. the line shows the voltage is steady and in **one direction** and therefore the current will also be steady and in one direction. A battery is a d.c. (**direct current**) supply.

For a.c. the wave shows the **voltage varies** between 0 and a peak voltage. The **direction** of the voltage also **reverses**. The current also **varies** in **size** and **direction**. The mains is an a.c. (**alternating current**) supply.

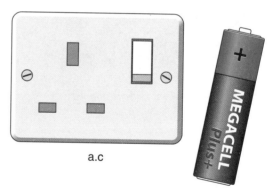

a.c

d.c

Mains voltage

The **frequency** of the mains is **50 Hz**.

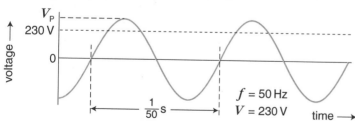

voltage

V_P

230 V

0

$\frac{1}{50}$ s

$f = 50$ Hz

$V = 230$ V

time

There are 50 complete waves every second. The flow of electrons increases and decreases, then increases and decreases in the opposite direction, 50 times every second. (Each complete cycle lasts 1/50 s.)

Peak and quoted values

- An **a.c. voltage** only ever reaches its **peak** value (Vp) for a **brief** moment in time and is **not** a measure of the effective voltage.

- The **quoted value** gives the **effective** voltage. An a.c. voltmeter will show the quoted voltage.

- The **quoted voltage** of a.c. will deliver the **same energy every second** as a d.c. voltage, that is, both will deliver the **same power**.

- The **quoted** value of an alternating voltage is always **less** than its **peak** value.

- The **quoted** value of the **mains** is **230 V**. The **peak** voltage is about **325 V**.

If a power supply has a peak voltage of 10 V, its dial will be set at 7 V. The quoted value is 7 V.

A 7 V battery would supply the same energy.

Top Tip
Remember to use a.c. meters with a.c. supplies!

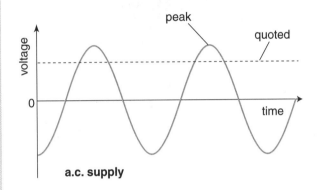

a.c. supply

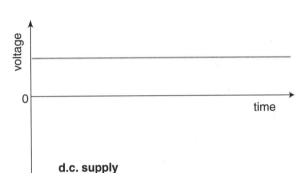

d.c. supply

Top Tip
The CRO measures voltage on the y-axis and time on the x-axis.

Top Tip
In a.c. graphs, above the 0 axis is increase in one direction, below the 0 axis is increase in the opposite direction.

Quick Test

1. What is the frequency of the Scottish mains supply?
2. Which is less, peak or quoted value?
3. If a battery is reversed, what happens to its signal on the CRO?
4. If the peak value of voltage is 5 V, what is the quoted value?
5. If the y gain on a CRO is set at 5 V/cm and the peak voltage is 10 V, how many cm will the signal rise from the origin?
6. A 6 V battery supplies the same power as 6 V peak a.c. TRUE or FALSE?

Answers 1. 50 Hz **2.** Quoted **3.** The line goes to the other side of 0. **4.** 3.5 V **5.** 2 cm **6.** False

Magnetic fields and electromagnetic induction

Magnets

The Earth has a **magnetic field** around it.

When a **permanent magnet** is suspended, it **aligns** itself in the Earth's magnetic field.

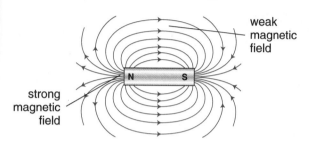

weak magnetic field

strong magnetic field

A magnet has **two poles**: **North** and **South**.

The North pole is a **North seeking pole** and the South pole is a **South seeking pole**.

The poles of magnets either attract or repel each other.

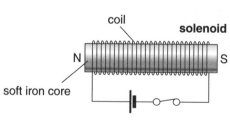

similar poles repel

opposite poles attract

N N

S N

LIKE POLES REPEL

UNLIKE POLES ATTRACT

Electromagnets

Oersted, 1820, discovered that when there is a **current** in a straight wire, there is a **circular magnetic field** round the wire.

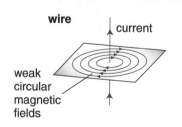

wire

current

weak circular magnetic fields

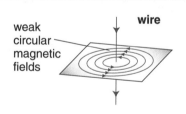

weak circular magnetic fields

wire

When electrons flow **away**, the field is **anti-clockwise** ('bye-bye anti').

To make the **magnetic field stronger** we can **increase the current** or make the wire into a **coil**.

If a coil is wrapped around an **iron core**, the magnetic field strength increases. This is an electromagnet.

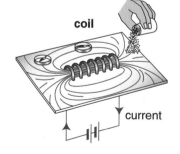

coil

current

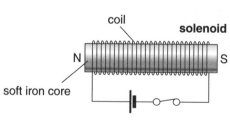

coil

solenoid

N   S

soft iron core

The magnetic field strength is increased with **more turns** and **more current**.

Inducing voltage in a conductor

Method 1) A **conductor moving** in a **magnetic field**.

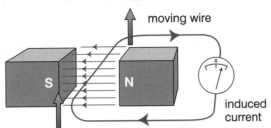

moving wire

induced current

- A wire is **moved** across a magnetic field. **Voltage** and **current** are induced.
- **Reversing** the movement reverses the **direction** of induced voltage and current.
- **No** movement => **No** voltage or current.
- The **induced voltage** can be **increased** by:
  a) **increasing** the **field strength** (stronger magnet);
  b) **moving** the conductor **quicker**.

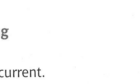

Top Tip
The magnetic field can also be moved across the stationary wire to induce voltage.

Method 2) A **conductor** is **in** a **changing** magnetic field.

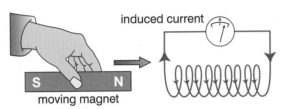

induced current

moving magnet

- When a **magnet is moved** towards a coil, the coil experiences a **changing magnetic field**. Voltage and current are **induced**.
- Moving the magnet away **reverses** the direction of induced voltage and current.
- The induced voltage can be increased by:
  a) increasing the **field strength** (stronger magnet);
  b) increasing the **speed of movement**;
  c) putting more **turns** on the coil.

Producing voltages in this way is known as **ELECTROMAGNETIC INDUCTION**.

Top Tip
It is the relative speed which is important. Magnet to coil or coil to magnet.

Quick Test

1. What do like magnetic poles do?
2. What is the direction of the magnetic field when electrons are coming towards you?
3. Name two ways of inducing voltage.
4. Give three ways to increase the strength of an induced voltage in a coil.

Answers 1. Repel **2.** Clock-wise **3.** a) Move a conductor in a magnetic field, b) Put a conductor in a changing magnetic field. **4** a) increase the field strength (stronger magnet); b) increase the speed of movement; c) put more turns on the coil.

Transformers and the grid

Transformers

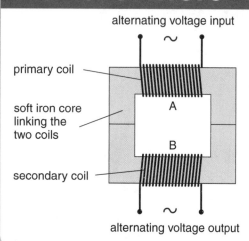

alternating voltage input

primary coil

soft iron core linking the two coils

secondary coil

alternating voltage output

A **transformer** consists of **two coils** of wire, usually linked by a **soft iron core**.

- An **alternating voltage (a.c.)** is applied across the **primary coil** to create a **changing magnetic field**.
- The **secondary coil** sits in the **changing magnetic field** and voltage (a.c.) is **induced** across this coil.

> **Top Tip**
> The two circuits are only linked magnetically, not electrically.

> **Top Tip**
> The iron core increases the effect by concentrating the field.

Voltages, currents and number of turns

Transformers are used to **change the size** of **a.c.** voltages and currents.

Voltage and number of turns

The **primary** (input) and **secondary** (output) voltages are linked by the **turns ratio**:

(n = number of turns) $\dfrac{n_s}{n_p} = \dfrac{V_s}{V_p}$

If a transformer is used to **increase voltage**, it is a **step-up** transformer. If the **voltage is decreased**, it is a **step-down** transformer.

e.g. A transformer with 2000 turns in the primary and 100 turns in the secondary is used with mains input. What is the output voltage?

V mains = 230 V. $\dfrac{n_s}{n_p} = \dfrac{V_s}{V_p}$ $\dfrac{100}{2000} = \dfrac{V_s}{230}$

2000 V_s = 230 × 100

V_s = 11.5 V

V_p

N_p turns

N_s turns

V_s

230 V_{ac}

2000 turns

100 turns

11.5 V_{ac}

Power, voltage and current:

In an **ideal transformer** (100% efficient, no energy loss)

Input power = Output power
$I_p V_p = I_s V_s$

or $\dfrac{V_s}{V_p} = \dfrac{I_p}{I_s}$ also $\dfrac{n_s}{n_p} = \dfrac{I_p}{I_s}$

When the voltage is stepped up, the current goes down. There is no gain or change of power.

Summary equations:

Input power $P_i = I_p V_p$ Output power $P_o = I_s V_s$ $\dfrac{n_s}{n_p} = \dfrac{V_p}{V_s} = \dfrac{I_p}{I_s}$

> **Top Tip**
> Cross multiply and solve with transformer equations.

The national grid

Long **transmission lines** between the power station and our homes and industries carry electrical energy.

Long transmission lines have **resistance** and there is **power loss** in the lines, which depends on the **square of the current**.

$$P_{loss} = I^2R$$

This loss is kept to a minimum by **increasing the voltage** using a **step-up** transformer so that the **current is decreased**. Near our homes the voltage is decreased to a safe level by a **step-down** transformer.

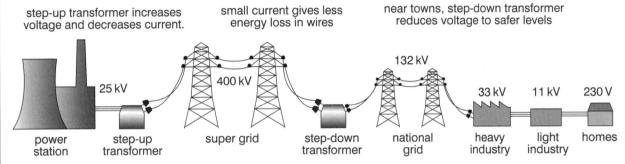

step-up transformer increases voltage and decreases current.

small current gives less energy loss in wires

near towns, step-down transformer reduces voltage to safer levels

25 kV   400 kV   132 kV   33 kV   11 kV   230 V

power station   step-up transformer   super grid   step-down transformer   national grid   heavy industry   light industry   homes

pylons keep high voltage away from people

lower voltage supply

A model **transmission system**:

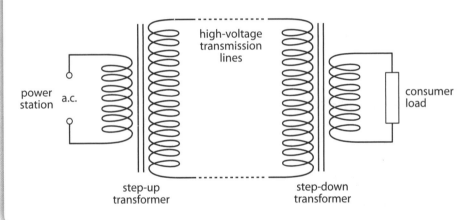

power station   a.c.

high-voltage transmission lines

consumer load

step-up transformer

step-down transformer

Top Tip
The greater the distance energy has to travel, the higher the voltage will be stepped up.

Top Tip
There will be several stages of transformers in the National Grid to get the different voltages required.

Quick Test

1. Why is a.c. used with transformers?

2. What kind of transformer: **a)** increases voltages? **b)** increases currents?

3. What is the input voltage applied to a transformer if the output is 5 V and the primary has 400 turns and the secondary has 100 turns on the coils.

4. If the primary voltage is 230 V and primary current is 0.4 A, what is the current through the load when the secondary voltage is 40 V?

5. Why is electrical energy transmitted through the National Grid at high voltages with low currents?

Output devices

Output devices take an electrical signal from the circuit and transform it into some useful form of energy, such as light, sound or kinetic (movement).

$\longrightarrow$ = 'is transformed to'

Output devices

The loudspeaker

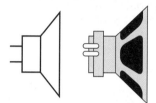

Electrical energy $\longrightarrow$ sound energy

The loudspeaker can handle continuously varying loudness and frequency. It is an analogue device.

Loudspeakers are used in hi-fi, radio, TV, phones and computers.

The electric motor

Electrical energy $\longrightarrow$ kinetic energy

The electric motor can continuously vary its speed. It is an analogue device.

Electric motors are used in washing dryers, CD players, printers and windscreen wipers.

The moving coil meter

Electrical energy $\longrightarrow$ kinetic energy

The moving coil meter can continuously vary its pointer. It is an analogue device.

Moving coil meters are used in ammeters, voltmeters and electric speedometers.

The relay

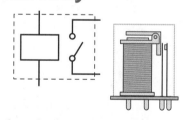

Electrical energy $\longrightarrow$ kinetic energy

The relay has a coil of wire whose magnetic field operates the opening or closing of a switch. It is a digital device. Relays are used in cars in many places. A low power circuit is used to switch a high power circuit.

The solenoid

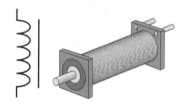

Electrical energy $\longrightarrow$ kinetic energy

The solenoid provides a straight line movement. An electromagnetic field from a coil pushes a bar, out or in. It is a digital device. Solenoids are used in a car for the starter and to operate the locks of a central locking system.

The light emitting diode (LED)

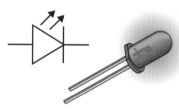

Electrical energy $\longrightarrow$ light energy

An LED light conducts and is on if connected one way or off if connected the other way. It is a digital device. LEDs are used in hi-fis, computers, fridges and 7-segment displays.

Top Tip
List the output devices in your home and their energy transformations.

Using the LED

Light emitting diodes (LED)

LEDs are made from **two semi-conductor materials**. When electrons cross the **junction** in the correct direction it **emits light**. The **diode symbol** has to 'point' **from + to –** from a power supply.

Connected the 'wrong' way round = OFF.   Connected the 'correct' way round = ON.

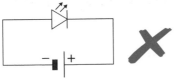

The **LED** operates with a **small voltage and current**, typically **2 V** and **10 mA**. A **resistor** normally has to be connected **in series** with the LED to **protect** it from high supplies.

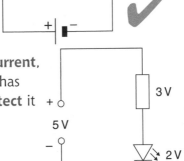

5 V

3 V

2 V

10 mA

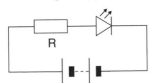

R

Top Tip
The LED is a modern output device. Find its many uses.

The current through the LED and the resistor is the same as they are both in series. The voltage across the resistor = the supply voltage minus the LED voltage.

$$R = \frac{V}{I} = \frac{(5-2)}{0.010} = \frac{3}{0.010} = 300\,\Omega$$

The LED gives out less light and has only one colour, but uses less energy and gives out no heat, compared with a filament lamp. It is also much more robust.

The 7-segment display

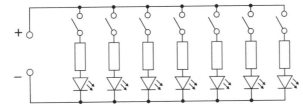

The **7-segment display** uses **7 LEDs**. Each LED can be operated independently. (Liquid Crystal Displays, LCDs, are also used.)

Quick Test

1. What type of energy do output devices convert?

2. Name 2 analogue output devices.

3. Why is a relay a digital device?

4. How does the 'arrow' on the symbol for the LED get connected when it is on?

5. A typical LED is connected to a 6 V supply. What value of resistor is required to protect it?

6. What number is formed when all 7 segments of a 7-segment display are on?

Input devices

Converting the world to electrical signals!

Converting to electrical energy

Devices which generate **electrical** energy directly **from sound**, **heat** and **light**.

The microphone

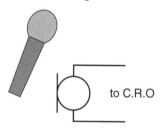

to C.R.O

Sound energy ⟶
electrical energy

The thermocouple

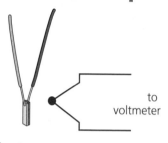

to voltmeter

Heat energy ⟶
electrical energy

The solar cell

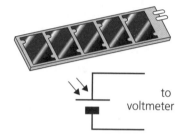

to voltmeter

Light energy ⟶
electrical energy

Controlling electrical energy

Devices where the **input** alters the **voltage** of an electrical supply.

The thermistor

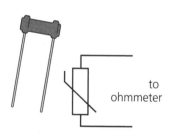

to ohmmeter

As the temperature increases, its resistance decreases

The light dependant resistor (LDR)

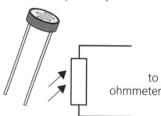

to ohmmeter

As the light increases, its resistance decreases

The voltage divider

The **voltage** from a supply is **divided** across 2 resistors in the ratio of these resistors.

$$\frac{V_1}{V_2} = \frac{R_1}{R_2}$$

If R_1 or R_2 varies, $V_1 : V_2$ is changed.

R_1 or R_2 can be replaced with a thermistor, or an LDR.

V will be the **input** to our **process** section.

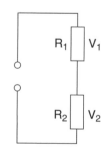

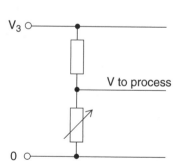

Voltage dividers with an input sensor

Putting an **input sensor** in series with a resistor allows light or heat to alter a voltage.

Voltage divider with a thermistor

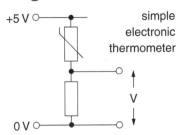

simple
electronic
thermometer

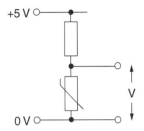

1) As **temperature increases**,
   $R_{thermistor}$ decreases => $V_{thermistor}$ decreases,
   => V increases

2) As **temperature increases**,
   $R_{thermistor}$ decreases => V decreases

Voltage divider with a LDR

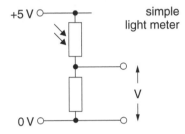

simple
light meter

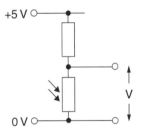

1) As **light increases**,
   R_{LDR} decreases => V_{LDR} decreases,
   => V increases

2) As **light increases**,
   R_{LDR} decreases, => V decreases

Top Tip
When light or heat go up, the resistance goes down in these two sensors.

Quick Test

1. What is the energy change in a solar cell?

2. What happens to the resistance of an LDR as the light decreases?

3. What is the symbol for a thermistor?

4. In a voltage divider what ratio does the voltage ratio copy?

5. A 12 V supply is divided by a 5 Ω and a 1 Ω resistor in series. What is the voltage across the 1 Ω?

Answers 1. Light energy to electrical energy **2.** Increases **3.** See above. **4.** R1:R2 **5.** 2V

Transistor processes

The NPN transistor

The transistor can be used as an **electronic switch**.

If it is **ON it conducts** and allows a current.

If it is **OFF it does not conduct** and there is no current.

When the voltage across the base-emitter of the NPN transistor, $V_{be} > 0.7\,V$, then the transistor conducts across collector-emitter and is ON.

When the voltage across the base-emitter of the NPN transistor, $V_{be} < 0.7\,V$ or negative, then the transistor does not conduct across collector-emitter and is OFF.

Top Tip

Transistor switching is at the heart of modern electronics and computers.

Light controlled circuits

1) This circuit switches the LED on when it gets dark.

Cover the LDR:

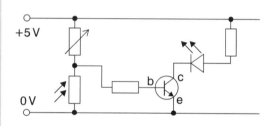

- Cover the LDR
- as light decreases
- R_{LDR} increases
- V_{LDR} increases $> 0.7\,V$
  - transistor switches to conduct
  - LED goes ON

The LED will also switch **off** when it is light. Describe how the circuit does this.

2) This circuit switches the LED **off** when it gets dark.

Cover the LDR:

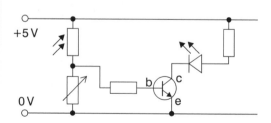

- As light decreases
- R_{LDR} increases
- V_{LDR} increases
- $V_{variable\ R}$ decreases $< 0.7\,V$
  - transistor does not conduct
  - LED goes OFF.

The LED will also switch **on** when it is light. Describe how the circuit does this.

The variable resistor

In the above circuits the variable resistor is used to allow the **light level** at which the transistor **switches** to be **adjusted**.

In the following circuits the variable resistor is used to allow the **temperature level** at which the transistor **switches** to be **adjusted**.

Temperature controlled circuits

1) This circuit switches the relay and a mains powered heater motor **off** when it gets hot.

Warm the thermistor:

- As temperature increases
- $R_{thermistor}$ decreases
- $V_{thermistor}$ decreases $< 0.7\,V$
  - transistor does not conduct
  - relay and motor go OFF.

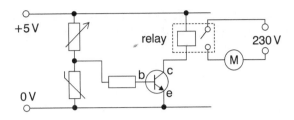

The heater motor will also switch **on** when it is cold. Describe how the **circuit** does this.

2) This circuit switches the relay and a mains powered fan motor **on** when it gets hot.

Warm the thermistor:

- As temperature increases
- $R_{thermistor}$ decreases
- $V_{thermistor}$ decreases
- $V_{variable\ R}$ increases $> 0.7\,V$
  - transistor switches to conduct
  - relay and fan go ON.

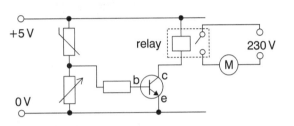

The fan will also switch **off** when it is cold. Describe how the circuit does this.

Top Tip
The NPN circuits could all be drawn with a MOSFET.

The MOSFET transistor

The MOSFET (**m**etal **o**xide **s**emiconductor **f**ield **e**ffect **t**ransistor) is an alternative transistor which can also be used as an electronic switch. The switching or gate voltage is about 2 V.

When the voltage across the gate-source of the MOSFET transistor, $Vgs > 2\,V$, then the transistor conducts across drain-source and is ON.

When the **voltage** across the **gate-source** of the MOSFET transistor, **$Vgs < 2\,V$ or negative**, then the transistor does **not conduct** across **drain-source** and is **OFF**.

This circuit switches a motor on when it gets hot.

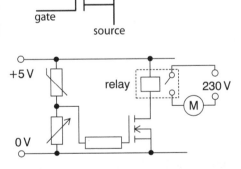

Quick Test

1. What is the main purpose of a transistor in electronics?

2. Why is a LDR in series with a resistor at the input stage?

3. What is the purpose of the variable resistor?

4. Name two types of transistor.

5. How does the MOSFET circuit above work?

Amplifiers and voltage gain

Amplifiers

The process of an **amplifier** is to increase the **strength** of an **electrical** signal.

Amplifiers are found in many devices:
Radio and television transmission and reception, hi-fi systems, hearing aids, mobile phones, camcorders, electrical and optical signal repeaters, satellite communication, megaphones, PA systems, baby alarms, after musical instrument pickups and after many input devices for heat, light and sound where only a small voltage is produced.

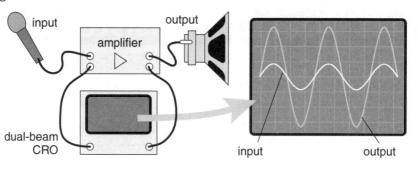

Amplifier gain

The purpose of an **amplifier** is to increase the **amplitude** of an **electrical** signal.

Only the amplitude should change.

The output signal of an audio amplifier should have the same frequency as, but a larger amplitude than, the input signal.

There should be **no change in frequency** or pattern or the signal is said to have **distortion**.

input   output
amplifier
dual-beam CRO
input   output

An amplifier works with a **power supply**. The power supply **provides the energy** for the bigger signal.
Basically the pattern of the input signal is transferred to the larger electrical supply signal.
In audio devices such as radios, televisions and hi-fis, the **volume control** operates the amplifier.
A series of transistors are built into an integrated circuit in modern amplifiers.

In a **PA (public address) system** a mixer or pre-amp will make sure all the input signals are balanced ready for the power amplifier:

The input signal to an amplifier is often measured in **mV**.

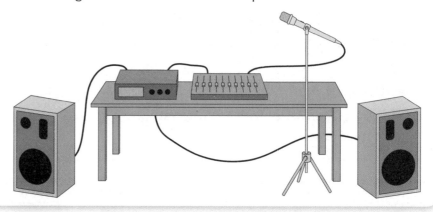

Voltage gain

The **voltage input** and the **voltage output** can be compared using oscilloscopes or multi-meters.

The **voltage gain** of an amplifier is then found from:

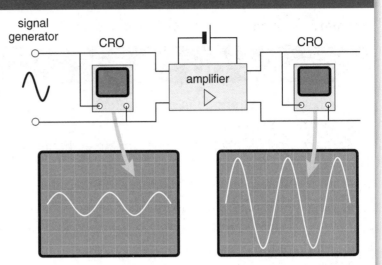

Voltage Gain = $\dfrac{\text{Voltage Output}}{\text{Voltage Input}}$

Gain = $\dfrac{V_{out}}{V_{in}}$

As **gain** is a **ratio**, there are **no units** for gain.

A weak voltage signal in an electronic system can be increased, e.g. TV aerial booster.

Example

Calculate the gain of an amplifier with input voltage 30 mV and output voltage 6 V.

Voltage Gain = $\dfrac{\text{Voltage Output}}{\text{Voltage Input}}$ = $\dfrac{6}{0.030}$ = 200

Example

If the gain of an amplifier is 50 and the input is 10 mV, what is the output voltage?

Voltage Gain = $\dfrac{\text{Voltage Output}}{\text{Voltage Input}}$

50 = $\dfrac{\text{Voltage Output}}{0.010}$

Voltage Output = 50 × 0.0010 = 0.50 V

Top Tip
Remember: Gain has no units!

Quick Test

1. What type of signal does an amplifier increase?
2. List four devices that use an amplifier.
3. What happens to the frequency of the signal during amplification?
4. What part of a signal is amplified in an amplifier?
5. What happens to the number of waves in and out of an amplifier?
6. The voltage input to an amplifier is 10 mV and the output voltage is 1.5 V. What is the gain?
7. If the gain is 20 and the input voltage is 0.2 V, what is the output voltage?

Answers 1. Electrical **2.** See list above. **3.** No change **4.** Amplitude or height **5.** No change **6.** 150 **7.** 4 V

Intermediate 2 Physics
Key facts and questions

Summary questions and answers. Fuller answers are obtained by referring back to the revision notes.

Circuits pp 30–37

1. What can electrons do in a conductor?
2. Describe electric current.
3. Draw circuit symbols: ammeter, voltmeter, battery, resistor, variable resistor, fuse, switch, lamp.
4. What is voltage?
5. What happens if there is an increase in resistance in a circuit?
6. How are ammeters and voltmeters connected?
7. What are the rules for current and voltage in a series circuit?
8. What are the rules for current and voltage in a parallel circuit?
9. What is Ohm's law?
10. What is the total of resistances in series and in parallel?
11. What is a potential divider?

Answers

1. Electrons are free to move in a conductor (metals and carbon). In an insulator the electrons are all bound in the atom (plastics, wood, rubber).
2. Current is the rate at which charge flows.

$$I = \frac{Q}{t} \text{ or } Q = It$$

Current I is the amount of charge Q passing in unit time t (1 s).

3. Check p 33.
4. The voltage of a supply is a measure of the energy given to the charges in a circuit.
5. There is a decrease in current.
6. An ammeter is placed in line (in series) with the circuit. A voltmeter is placed across (in parallel with) the component being measured.
7. The current is the same at all points of a series circuit. The sum of the voltages across the components in series is equal to the supply voltage.

Series: $I_S = I_1 = I_2 = I_3$
$$V_S = V_1 + V_2 + V_3$$

8. The sum of the currents in parallel branches is equal to the current drawn from the supply. The voltages across components in parallel are the same and equal to their supply.

Parallel: $I_S = I_1 + I_2 + I_3$
$$V_S = V_1 = V_2 = V_3$$

9. The ratio V/I remains approximately constant for different currents.
$$R = \frac{V}{I} \text{ or } V = IR$$

10. Resistance increases in series:
$$R_T = R_1 + R_2 + R_3$$
Resistance decreases in parallel:
$$\frac{1}{R_T} = \frac{1}{R_1} + \frac{1}{R_2} + \frac{1}{R_3}$$

11. A potential divider consists of a number of resistors, or a variable resistor, connected across a supply. The voltage divides in the ratio of the resistors:
$$\frac{V_1}{V_2} = \frac{R_1}{R_2}$$

Electrical energy pp 38–41

1. What transformation happens when there is an electrical current in a component?
2. What is power?
3. What is the energy transformation in a lamp?
4. Where does the energy transformation in a heater occur?
5. What is d.c.? What is a.c.?
6. What are the values of the mains supply?
7. How does the quoted value of a.c. compare with its peak voltage? How does it compare with d.c.?

Answers

1. When there is an electrical current in a component, there is an energy transformation.
2. Power is the amount of energy transformed in unit time, the electrical energy transformed each second.

$$P = \frac{E}{t} \qquad P = IV \qquad P = I^2R \qquad P = \frac{V^2}{R}$$

3. Electrical energy is transformed into light and heat energy in a lamp.
4. The energy transformation in an electrical heater occurs in the resistance wire.
5. d.c. is a current in one direction. a.c. is a current which varies in size and direction.
6. Frequency = 50 Hz. Quoted Voltage = 230 V.
7. The quoted voltage of a.c. is less than its peak voltage. The quoted voltage gives the same power to a resistor as a d.c. supply voltage.

Electromagnetism pp 42–45

1. What exists around a current-carrying wire?
2. When will voltage be induced in a conductor?
3. What affects the size of induced voltage?
4. What are transformers used for?
5. What are the transformer equations?

Answers

1. A magnetic field exists around a current-carrying wire.
2. When wires are moving between magnetic poles, across a magnetic field. When a magnet is moved near a coil, the conductor is in a changing magnetic field.
3. The field strength, the number of turns on a coil, the relative speed of movement.
4. Transformers are used to change the magnitude of an alternating voltage.
5. $P_{in} = I_p V_p$ $P_{out} = I_s V_s$ $\frac{n_s}{n_p} = \frac{V_s}{V_p} = \frac{I_p}{I_s}$

Electronic components pp 46–53

1. Give examples of output devices and their energy transformations.
2. Draw the LED symbol. Label the correct way round to power it.
3. What is the value of the series resistor used to protect the LED from high voltage?
4. Give examples of input devices and their energy transformations.
5. What do thermistors do as temperature increases?
6. What do LDRs do as light increases?
7. An LDR or thermistor sensor is in series with a resistor across a supply voltage. What does the voltage across the sensor do as light or temperature increase?
8. Draw the n-channel MOSFET symbol.
9. Draw the NPN transistor symbol.
10. What can a transistor be used for?
11. Explain the operation of a transistor switching circuit.
12. List devices which contain amplifiers.
13. What changes when using an amplifier?
14. What is the voltage gain equation for an amplifier?
15. What are the units of voltage gain?

Answers

1. Give for lamp, loudspeaker, relay, LED, 7-segment display and others from p 46. Energy change is always from electrical.
2.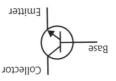
3. e.g.: $R = \frac{\text{(supply voltage} - \text{LED voltage)}}{\text{typical LED current}}$
= $(5 - 2)/0.010 = 300\ \Omega$
4. Give for microphone, thermocouple, solar cell, thermistor and LDR from p 48. Energy change is always to electrical.
5. As the temperature increases, the resistance decreases.
6. As the light increases, the resistance decreases.
7. Resistance of sensor decreases, so sensor voltage decreases.
8.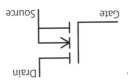
9.
10. The transistor can be used as an electronic switch.
11. When the voltage across the base-emitter of the NPN transistor, $V_{be} > 0.7$ V, then the transistor conducts across collector-emitter and is ON.
12. Radio and television transmission and reception, hifi systems, hearing aids, mobile phones, camcorders, electrical and optical signal repeaters, satellite communication, megaphones, PA systems, baby alarms and after musical instrument pickups.
13. The output signal of an audio amplifier should have the same frequency as, but a larger amplitude than, the input signal.
14. Voltage Gain = $\frac{\text{Voltage Output}}{\text{Voltage Input}}$
15. There are no units! Gain = $\frac{V_{out}}{V_{in}}$

Speed of waves

Waves

Waves and optics are used throughout the telecommunications, electrical and medical industries.

There are many types of waves including

- **water** waves
- **sound** waves
- **light**, **radio** and other waves making the **electromagnetic spectrum.**

A wave is a movement of energy.

A wave transfers energy.

Energy moves **across** the ocean and the **water moves up and down**.

Sound energy travels through the air and the **particles vibrate**.

Radio waves can travel through **space** as well as through the air.

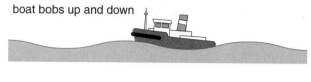

boat bobs up and down

loudspeaker vibrates

air particles vibrate

Thunder and lightning

We see the lightning flash, then we hear the thunder. **Light** travels so fast, it takes **virtually no time** at all to reach us!

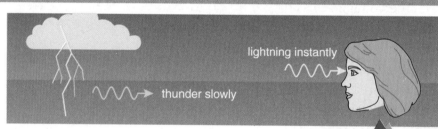

lightning instantly

thunder slowly

The speed of light is almost **1 million times faster** than the speed of sound.

speed of light, v_{light} = 300 000 000 m/s = 3×10^8 m/s.

speed of sound, v_{sound} = 340 m/s = 3.4×10^2 m/s.

We can work out how far away the thunderstorm is using the speed of sound alone.

Top Tip

Sound needs particles (solid, liquid or gas) to travel through. Light can travel in a vacuum.

Calculating wave speed

Speed is defined as the **distance travelled in unit time (1 s)**.

$speed = \dfrac{distance}{time}$	$v = \dfrac{d}{t}$	distance = speed × time $d = vt$

where v = speed in m/s, d = distance travelled in m, t = time taken in s

e.g. During a thunderstorm there was a delay of 20 s between the lightning flash and the clap of thunder. How far away was the storm?

$d = v \times t = 340 \times 20 = 6800$ m.

Sound and light signals both transfer energy.

Measuring the speed of sound

Method 1:

We can measure the speed of sound in air **in the lab**.

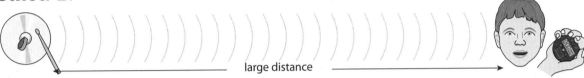

- Measure a distance, say 1 m.
- Place 2 microphones this distance apart attached to a 'millisecond timer' or computer and interface.
- The timer starts **timing** when the sharp sound of the hammer passes microphone 1 and stops timing when the sound passes microphone 2.
- Then **calculate** using $v = d/t$.

Method 2:

We can measure the speed of sound in air **in the open air**.

We see the drumstick hit the cymbal. We hear the sound a short time after this. The **time interval** is recorded with a stopwatch. The **distance** from the source to our ears is recorded with a measuring tape. Speed, calculated using $v = d/t$ gives around 340 m/s.

Top Tip

With echos, the distance measured has to be doubled or the time is halved.

Method 3:

We can measure the speed of sound in air **echoing from a wall**.

The **clap-echo time** is recorded. The **distance** travelled by the sound is double the distance to the wall.

The **speed** is the distance to wall divided by half the clap-echo time.

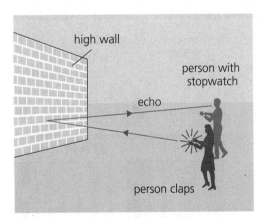

Quick Test

1. What is a wave?

2. When waves move across the ocean, what does the water do?

3. If thunder is heard 3 s after a lightning flash, how far away is the strike?

4. How long does light take to travel 1 km?

5. Describe how to measure the speed of sound in the lab.

6. If sound takes 1 s from source – echo from a cliff – how far away is the cliff?

Answers 1. A transfer of energy. **2.** Move up and down. **3** $d = vt = 340 \times 3 = 1020\,\text{m}$. **4** $3.3 \times 10^{-6}\text{s}$. **5** See above method 1. **6** 170 m.

Examining waves

Longitudinal or transverse

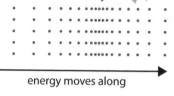

Top Tip
Sound is longitudinal, the rest are transverse.

Longitudinal

Sound is a **longitudinal** wave. The vibrations are **in line** with the direction of movement of energy.

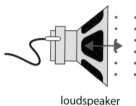 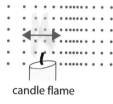 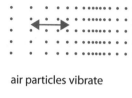

loudspeaker   candle flame   air particles vibrate   energy moves along

Transverse

Water and the **electromagnetic waves** are **transverse**. The vibrations are at **right angles** to the direction of movement of energy. A wave can be sent along a rope to illustrate a transverse wave.

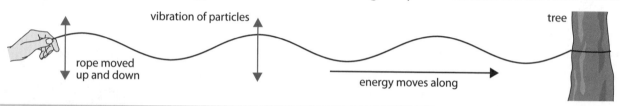

vibration of particles — tree
rope moved up and down — energy moves along

Waves in the ripple tank

Transverse water waves can be studied in the ripple tank. The frequency of the motor and rod is the same as the frequency of the water waves. **Increase the frequency to decrease the wavelength.**

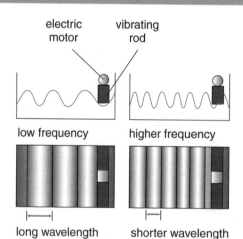

electric motor — vibrating rod
low frequency — higher frequency
long wavelength — shorter wavelength

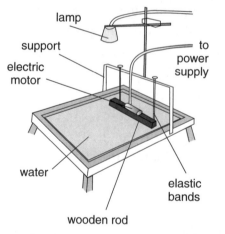

lamp — support — to power supply — electric motor — water — wooden rod — elastic bands

Slinky vibrations

The slinky can illustrate **longitudinal** and **transverse** waves.

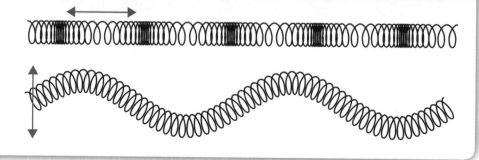

Measuring a wave

		Measured in...
Wavelength (λ):	The **distance till a wave repeats** itself.	metres, m
Amplitude (a):	The **height from the rest** position.	metres, m
Period (T):	The **time for 1 wave** (to pass a point).	seconds, s

If 2 waves pass a point in a second, the period of each wave is $\frac{1}{2}$ s.

If 3 waves pass a point in a second, the period of each wave is $\frac{1}{3}$ s.

If 10 waves pass a point in 2 seconds, the time for 1 wave is $\frac{2}{10} = \frac{1}{5}$ s. $T = \frac{1}{5}$ s.

Frequency (f):	The **number of waves in unit time**. This gives the number of waves per second.	Hertz, Hz. 1 Hz = 1 wave/second.

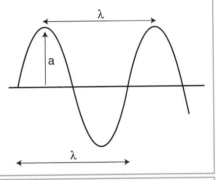

frequency = number / time

10 waves pass in 5 s. $\frac{10}{5} = 2$ waves pass in 1 s. $f = 2$ Hz.

frequency = 1 / Period

Waves pass every 0.2 s. $f = \frac{1}{0.2} = 5$ Hz.

Waves pass every $\frac{1}{2}$ s. $f = 1/0.5 = 2$ Hz.

Speed (v):	The **distance** travelled in **unit time**.	metres/second, m/s

$v = d/t$

The wave equation

Speed is related to frequency and wavelength.

Speed is equal to the product **frequency × wavelength**.

'The wave equation': $v = f\lambda$

frequency $\boxed{f = v/\lambda}$ wavelength: $\boxed{\lambda = v/f}$

Calculate the speed of a 50 Hz wave with a wavelength of 2 m.

$v = f\lambda = 50 \times 2 = 100$ m/s.

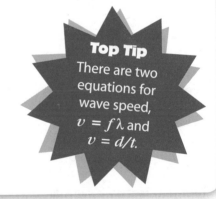

Top Tip

There are two equations for wave speed, $v = f\lambda$ and $v = d/t$.

Quick Test

1. What types of wave are longitudinal?

2. 10 waves are 5 m in total length. What is each wavelength?

3. From peak to trough a wave measures 60 cm. What is its amplitude?

4. A wave has a frequency of 10 Hz. What does this mean?

5. There are 20 waves passing a point in 4 s. What is the wave **a)** frequency, **b)** period?

6. A wave of frequency 5000 Hz and length 2 cm is travelling at what speed?

Answers 1. Sound waves **2.** 0.5 m **3.** 30 cm **4.** 10 waves / second **5. a)** 5 Hz **b)** 1/5 = 0.2 s **6.** 5000 × 0.02 = 100 m/s

The electromagnetic spectrum

Electromagnetic waves

James Clerk Maxwell was the famous Scottish physicist who discovered how a **changing magnetic field** coupled with a **changing electric field** to produce **moving electromagnetic waves**. Maxwell suggested in 1865 that light was electromagnetic energy and predicted more of the **electromagnetic radiation** we now call the **electromagnetic spectrum**.

The Electromagnetic Spectrum

				Frequency (Hz)	Wavelength (m)
Gamma	gamma ray		short wavelength, high frequency	10^{20}	10^{-12}
X-rays	x-ray			10^{18}	10^{-10}
Ultraviolet	uv specs			10^{15}	10^{-8}
Visible	ROY G BIV		violet indigo blue green yellow orange red	10^{14}	10^{-7}
Infra-red	heat rays, remote controls			10^{14}	10^{-6}
Microwave	radar			10^{11}	10^{-3}
TV and radio	TV/FM/AM		long wavelength, low frequency	10^{6}	10^{3}

Heinrich **Hertz**, a German scientist, proved the existence of radio waves and demonstrated that the speed of radio waves was equal to the speed of light, which Maxwell had predicted!

The **speed** of radio, television and light and all electromagnetic waves through air or space is 3×10^{8} m/s.

The **wave equation**, $v = f\lambda$ can be used with electromagnetic waves.

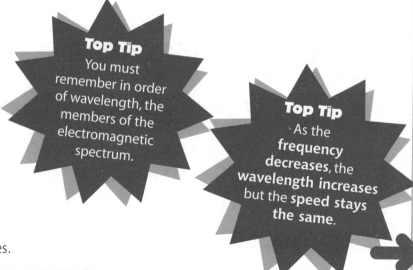

Top Tip
You must remember in order of wavelength, the members of the electromagnetic spectrum.

Top Tip
As the frequency decreases, the wavelength increases but the **speed stays the same**.

Additional information

Gamma rays

Natural materials such as some **rocks**, and **man made materials** such as can be found in power stations, can emit **gamma rays**. A lot of gamma rays are produced in the universe and are travelling through **space**. Gamma rays have **very high frequency**, **very short wavelength** and **high energy**. They can be detected with **photographic film** or a **geiger counter**. They can be used in **radioactive tracers** or to **kill cancer cells**. Instruments and syringes can be **sterilised** with gamma rays to kill the bacteria. They **penetrate** so well they can also be used to **detect cracks** in metals.

X-rays

X-rays have **high frequency** and **high energy**. X-rays are produced from **X-ray tubes**. Hot gases in **the universe** also emit X-rays. They can **penetrate tissue** and be detected on **photographic film**. Doctors and dentists use X-rays to examine our **bones** and **teeth**. Doctors can also look for **ulcers** in your **guts**. You swallow a Barium meal which **absorbs** X-rays. You can get ulcers by worrying about your exams, so don't worry, **do the revision** and **success** comes!

Ultraviolet

UV tubes and the **sun** are sources of **ultraviolet**. They cause certain materials, often white, to **fluoresce**. Although the atmosphere stops many of these rays reaching us on earth, they can cause our **sun tan** or give us **skin cancer**. Hidden marks on banknotes will **fluoresce** under a **UV lamp**. UV has a **higher frequency** and **energy** than visible light.

Visible light

Light is emitted from **hot filaments** of **lamps**, from **stars** and even fireflies. In physics, white is not a colour at all, but rather the combination of all the colours of the **visible light spectrum**. In 1672, when describing his discovery that light could be split into many colours by a prism, **Isaac Newton** gave the seven names red, orange, yellow, green, blue, indigo, violet. Violet has the shortest wavelength and red the longest.

Infra-red

Infra-red rays (**heat** waves) have a **lower frequency** than visible light rays. We know infra-red more as heat as it is detected on our **skin**. Infra-red rays are **absorbed** by our skin and we feel warm. **Invisible heat** rays are given out by all warm bodies. **Thermograms** are colour heat photos of this radiation. If an infra-red camera takes your photo you will not notice it as the rays are invisible. Burglars beware!

Microwaves

Above radio we find **microwaves** with a higher frequency (in the GHz range). Microwaves diffract (bend) very little though, compared with radio. Microwaves are sent to and from **satellites**. Microwaves are used from space by **astronomers** to find out about the **structure of galaxies**. Microwaves are used with **mobile phones** and for **cooking**. Some people worry that microwaves from their mobile phones will cook their brains.

TV and radio

TV and **radio** waves have the **longest wavelengths** in the electromagnetic spectrum. They **diffract** (bend) round obstacles to get to our homes. **Transmitters** and **receivers** are used to send and detect these signals. Radio waves are also emitted by **stars** and **gases** in **space**. Radio waves tell us more about **matter** in the **universe**.

Quick Test

1. What waves have the lowest frequency?

2. What waves have the shortest wavelength?

3. What waves have the longest wavelength?

4. What waves have the highest frequency?

5. What is the order of these waves in increasing wavelength? Ultraviolet, TV and radio, gamma, microwave, X-rays, visible, infra-red.

Reflectors of light

Reflection from a plane mirror

Light is a **wave**.   Light can be **reflected**.   Light **rays** travel in **straight lines**.

A smooth, **shiny surface** such as a mirror makes a **good reflector**.
The **normal** is a line at right angles to the surface. The normal is **0°**.
The **angle of incidence** is measured between the normal and the incident ray.
The **angle of reflection** is measured between the normal and the reflected ray.

A ray box is directed to a plane mirror at five different angles of incidence as shown.

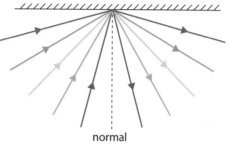

normal

Angle of incidence, i	Angle of reflection, r
15	
30	
45	
60	
75	

The law of reflection is: $i = r$

The **angle of incidence** is **equal** to the **angle of reflection**.

The angles of reflection are 15°, 30°, 45°, 60° and 75°.

Reflection from a curved surface

Curved reflectors are often used with **sound**, **infra-red**, **microwaves**, **TV signals** and **satellite communication** as well as with **light rays**.

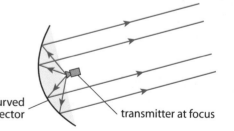

Receiving dish aerial

Curved reflectors are attached to **receiver aerials** to make the **signal stronger**. A **curved reflector** will **collect** and **reflect** many rays to a point called the **focus point**. The receiver aerial is placed at this point.

incoming parallel rays

receiving aerial is placed at focus

curved reflector

With a ray-box you will see the light rays will cross over at the focus point. It is bright at the focus.

Transmitting dish aerial

If a **transmitting aerial** is placed at the **focus point** of a curved reflector, a **parallel beam** of rays is sent out.

If a light bulb is placed in front of a curved reflector, a narrow beam of light is sent out. A **torch** and a **light house** are good examples.

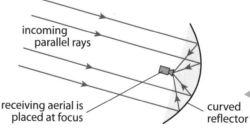
curved reflector

transmitter at focus

Car headlights place the filament near the focus to have a slight spread of light.

Size of dish

The **larger the area** of reflector dish (receiver or transmitter) the more rays are **collected** for reflection. The signal has **more energy** and is **stronger**.

Reversibility

The **principle of reversibility** of a ray path is that **ray paths** are **reversible**.

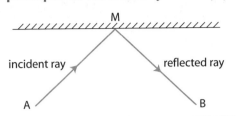
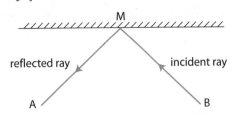

Microwaves

Microwaves are used for telecommunication as well as cooking!

Microwaves have higher frequencies (in the GHz range) than radio waves. Microwaves **diffract** (bend) so little they virtually travel in **straight lines**. Microwaves are easily **focused** using **dish aerials**. **Transmitter** and **receiver** dishes are in **line of sight**. Repeater towers are needed every 40 km or when a change in direction round an obstacle is needed.

The transmitter and receiver are placed at the **focal points** of the dishes. Between the receiver and the transmitter the signal is **amplified**. The signals are sent in **narrow beams**.

The speed of microwaves, $v_{microwaves} = 300\,000\,000\,\text{m/s} = 3 \times 10^8\,\text{m/s}$

Satellites

Communication round the world needs three satellites.

Microwaves are sent to and from **satellites**.

Each satellite has a **receiver** and **transmitter aerial** with **reflector dishes** and so does each ground station. The satellites and ground stations also **boost** the signal before **repeating** it.

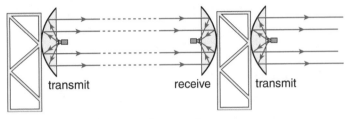

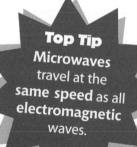

Top Tip
Microwaves travel at the **same speed** as all electromagnetic waves.

Quick Test

1. A light ray reflects off a surface at 50° from the normal. What was the angle of incidence?

2. What is meant by **a)** the normal, **b)** the angle of incidence and **c)** the angle of reflection?

3. What is the Law of Reflection?

4. At what point do all the waves from a dish aerial meet?

5. What does a bigger dish do?

6. What speed do microwaves travel at?

Optical fibres

Critical angle and total internal reflection

When light, travelling **through** glass, hits the **inner surface** of the glass it will either

1 go through and escape, undergoing a **refraction** (bending) or
2 the surface acts like a mirror, and the light is **reflected** and stays inside.

The angle of incidence decides whether light will refract out or reflect in.

1 The **angle of incidence is small**. The ray passes from glass to air and **refracts**.
2 The **angle of incidence is large**. The ray is reflected. This is known as **total internal reflection**.

The incident ray is at the **critical angle** when the ray changes from refracting out to total internal reflection. **At the critical angle the emerging ray is at 90°.**

Total internal reflection occurs when light travels in an optically dense material (**glass**) and meets the surface which is surrounded by a **less** optically dense material (**air**). **The light does not leave the glass.**

Top Tip
The critical angle is about 42° for normal glass.

Refraction

The angle of incidence i is small, **less** than the critical angle C.
The ray passes **out** of the glass and is **refracted**.

$i < C$

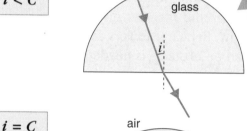

Critical angle

The angle of incidence i **is now equal** to the critical angle C.
The **angle of refraction is now 90°**.
The ray emerges along the glass block.
Some of the light is also reflected.

$i = C$

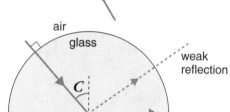

Total internal reflection

Angle of incidence i **is large, greater** than the critical angle C.
The ray is **totally internally reflected**.
The angle of reflection is **equal** to the angle of incidence.

$i > C$

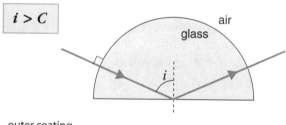

TIR in an optical fibre

Light travels along an **optical fibre** by **total internal reflections**. The fine glass fibre is always surrounded by a coating of **less** dense cladding glass. The central pure glass is about 0.01 mm in diameter and the cladding glass is about 0.1 mm in diameter. The less dense coating ensures that **no light escapes** and **TIR** always occurs. Usually a further outer coating is also applied.

A fibre optic light pipe is made of **bundles** of optical fibres.

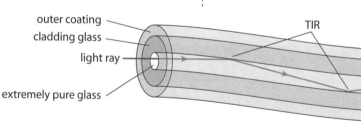

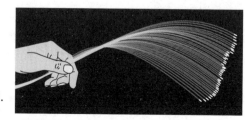

Optical fibres and their advantages

Optical fibres are very **pure**, **thin**, **flexible**, **glass rods**. The glass is so pure that if the sea was made of this glass we could see to the bottom! This means light can be sent **large distances** before repeaters are needed.

The transmitted light carries information, usually in a series of pulses.

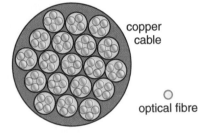

Top Tip
Optical fibres can carry **telephone, cable TV, videotext** and **computer signals**.

- The light travelling along inside the narrow optical fibre always hits the glass boundary at a **large angle**, **greater** than the critical angle.
- The light travels by a **series** of **total internal reflections**.

An optical fibre can carry a signal from a transmitter (T) to a receiver (R):

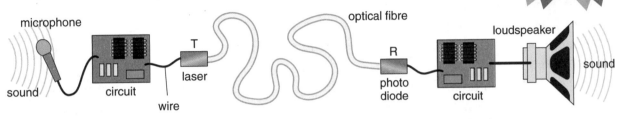

Advantages and disadvantages

- There is **little loss** of energy due to the pure glass.
- Very **few repeater** units are needed. Compare copper every 4 km, optical 100 km.
- Light can be sent over **long distances** optically.
- Optical signals are **free from electrical interference**.
- Optical cables are much **lighter** than electrical copper cables.
- They **cost less**.
- They carry **more signals**.
- Optical fibres transmit light at **high speed** – 2×10^8 m/s.
- The main disadvantage of optical fibres is they are **harder to join** than copper wires.

copper cable

optical fibre

Quick Test

1. When does light escape from glass?
2. What is the critical angle?
3. What is meant by total internal reflection?
4. What invention transmits light through an optical fibre?
5. What is done to stop light escaping from the glass?
6. Give five advantages of an optical fibre over copper cable.

Lenses

Refraction of light

Refraction occurs when light moves from one density of material **into** another.

When a ray of light is refracted there is a **change in velocity** and often a **change in direction**.

Plane rectangular block

The **normal** is a construction line drawn **perpendicular** through the boundary.

Angles are always measured from the normal.

- The **angle of incidence** i is measured between the normal and the incident ray.
- The **angle of refraction** r is measured between the normal and the refracted ray.
- Air to glass: When a ray of light enters a more dense medium it **slows down** and bends **towards** the normal.
- Glass to air: When a ray of light enters a less dense medium it **speeds up** and bends **away** from the normal.

If the ray enters the glass **on the normal**, it does not change direction but there is a **change in speed** entering and emerging from the glass.

ray bends **towards** the normal as it enters the glass

ray bends **away from** the normal as it leaves the block (parallel to the original ray)

Top Tip
Angles are smaller in the glass.

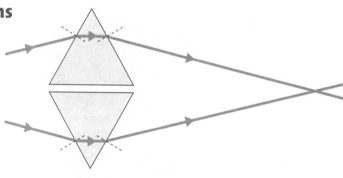

air   glass   air

3×10^8 m/s 2×10^8 m/s 3×10^8 m/s

Triangular prisms

A ray of light will bend towards the normal entering each prism and away from the normal emerging from each prism.

Top Tip
The two triangular prisms are similar to a convex lens.

Reversibility of light

Light rays are reversible:

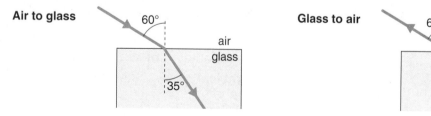

Air to glass   60°   air   glass   35°

Glass to air   60°   air   glass   35°

A ray enters glass at 60°, it will refract to 35°.
In reverse, the ray meeting the boundary at 35° leaves the glass at 60°.

Converging and diverging lenses

Top Tip
When drawing rays through a lens, draw the centre ray first. Its direction is unchanged.

Lenses are curved shapes of glass or plastic which **refract light**. A **converging** lens is thicker in the centre than its edges, while a **diverging** lens is thinner in the centre.

A **CONVERGING** lens refracts light so that the rays converge **to a focal point**.

A **DIVERGING** lens refracts light so that the rays diverge **as if away** from a **focal point**.

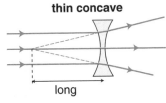

thin convex — principal focus — long focal length

thick convex — short

thin concave — long

thick concave — short

A **CONVEX** lens is a typical converging lens.

A **CONCAVE** lens is a typical diverging lens.

Lens power

Top Tip
A **powerful** lens has a **shorter** focal length.
When calculating the power of a lens, remember to use focal length in metres.

Thick lenses **bend (refract)** the light more than thin lenses and are said to be more powerful.

Power = 1/ focal length in metres	$P = 1/f$	$f = 1/P$

Power is measured in **dioptres, D**, focal length in **metres, m**.

Converging (convex) lenses have a **positive** power, e.g. $+10\,D$
Diverging (concave) lenses have a **negative** power, e.g. $-10\,D$.

A diverging lens has a focal length of 20 cm. What is its power?
$f = -20\,cm = -0.20\,m$ $P = 1/f = 1/-0.20 = -5\,D$

Optional experiment: To find the focal length of a spherical lens

When measuring focal length, the incident rays should be parallel. A **distant light source** such as a window is considered to have **parallel rays**. The distance from the spherical convex lens to the screen can be measured with a ruler. This is the **principal focal length**.

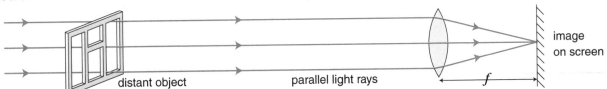

distant object — parallel light rays — f — image on screen

Quick Test

1. What is the speed of light in air? In glass?
2. What changes when light is refracted?
3. Name a type of converging lens.
4. What happens to light when it diverges?
5. A lens has a power of 2 D. How long is the focal length?
6. The focal length of a lens is 5 cm. What is its power?

Ray diagrams and eyesight

Ray diagrams

Ray diagrams are used to show how a converging lens can form an image with objects placed at different distances from the lens. The same lens can be used, but each position will have a different application.

Rules for ray diagrams: Two rays are drawn from the top of the object.

- A ray parallel to the principal axis bends through the principal focus point **f**.
- A ray through the centre of the lens goes straight through.
- The top of the image is found where these two rays meet.

1 The object is **more than two focal lengths** from the lens:

This is how a **camera** or the **eye** forms an image. The image is **real, inverted and diminished**.

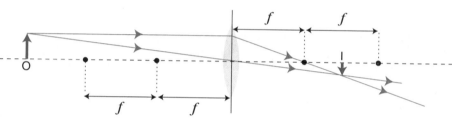

2 The object is **between one and two focal lengths** from the lens:

This is how a **projector** can form an image. The image is **real, inverted and magnified**.

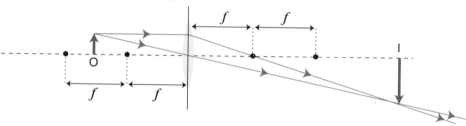

3 The object is **less than one focal length** in front of the lens:

This is how a **magnifying glass** forms an image with our eye and brain. Image is **virtual, upright and magnified**. The eye looks through the lens at the object but sees the image.

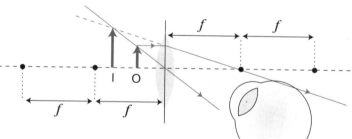

An image can be:

- **Real or virtual**
- **Upright or inverted**
- **Magnified, same size or diminished**

A **real** image is where the rays meet and a screen will form an image.

A **virtual** image is where the brain thinks of and sees the image but it is really focused on the retina of the eye!

$$\text{Magnification} = \frac{\text{length of image}}{\text{length of object}}$$

Top Tip
Practise drawing ray diagrams, accurately to scale.

Interesting question! In images from space, what is upright and what is inverted?

Long and short sight

The eye can be the wrong shape or the muscles do not adjust the lens enough.
Both **long and short sight** can be corrected using lenses.

To see objects clearly, light rays must be **focused on the retina**.

Long sight

A long-sighted person (usually older)
cannot see close up clearly.
The eye can be too short.
The eye lens can be too thin.

The incoming light is **focused beyond
the retina**.
A point becomes a BLUR on the retina.
This can be corrected with a **converging**
(convex) lens:

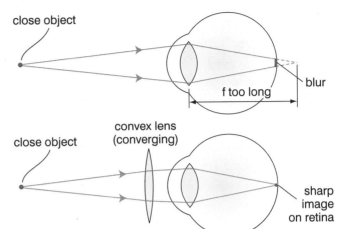

Short sight

A short-sighted person **cannot see far away clearly**.
The eye can be too long. The eye lens can be too fat.

The incoming light is **focused in front of the retina**.
A point becomes a BLUR on the retina.
This can be corrected with a **diverging** (concave) lens:

Top Tip
Long sight:
Focal length **too
long. Short** sight:
Focal length
too short.

Quick Test

1. How many rays are needed to construct an image?

2. What is an upside down image called?

3. Where in the eye is an image found?

4. Where is the object placed for a magnifying glass?

5. What type of lens corrects short sight?

6. What is wrong with the focal length of a long-sighted person?

Key facts and questions

Summary questions and answers. Fuller answers are obtained by referring back to the revision notes.

Waves pp 56–61

1. What does a wave do?
2. Describe how to measure the speed of sound in air.
3. What is the speed of radio and TV waves?
4. What is the relationship between distance, time and speed?
5. Define the following terms: wave, frequency, wavelength, speed, amplitude and period.
6. What is the difference between the two main groups of waves?
7. What is the relationship between speed, wavelength and frequency for waves?
8. State the members of the electromagnetic spectrum in order of wavelength, shortest first.

Answers

1. A wave transfers energy.
2. Measure a distance, say 1 m. Place 2 microphones this distance apart attached to a 'millisecond timer' or computer and interface. The timer starts timing when the sharp sound of the hammer passes microphone 1 and stops timing when the sound passes microphone 2. Then calculate using $v = d/t$. (See p 57 for alternatives.)
3. The same as light, 300 million m/s (3×10^8 m/s).
4. Speed is defined as the distance travelled in unit time (1 s). $v = \frac{d}{t}$ $d = v t$
5. Wave: A wave is a movement of energy.
   Frequency (f): The number of waves in unit time. Frequency is measured in Hertz, Hz.
   Wavelength (λ): The distance till a wave repeats itself. Wavelength is measured in metres, m.
   Speed (v): The distance travelled in unit time. Speed is measured in metres/second, m/s.
   Amplitude (A): The height from the rest position. Amplitude is measured in metres, m.
   Period (T): The time for 1 wave (to pass a point). Period is measured in seconds, s.
6. Longitudinal: Sound is a longitudinal wave. The vibrations are in line with the direction of movement of energy. Transverse: Water and the electromagnetic waves are transverse. The vibrations are at right angles to the direction of movement of energy.
7. Speed is equal to the product frequency × wavelength. The wave equation: $v = f \lambda$
8. Gamma ⟵ short wavelength, high frequency
   X-rays
   Ultraviolet
   Visible (ROYGBIV)
   Infra-red
   Microwave
   TV and radio ⟶ long wavelength, low frequency

Reflection pp 62–65

1. What can light do when it hits a shiny surface?
2. What measurements are made when light is reflected?
3. What is the principle of reversibility of a ray path?
4. What is the action of curved reflectors on received signals?
5. What is the action of curved reflectors on transmitted signals?
6. Describe an application of curved reflectors used in telecommunication.
7. Explain what is meant by total internal reflection.
8. Explain what is meant by the critical angle.
9. How does an optical fibre transmission system operate?

Answers

1. Light can be reflected.
2. The normal is a line at right angles to the surface. Angles are measured from the normal. The normal is 0°.
3. The angle of incidence is measured between the normal and the incident ray.
   The angle of reflection is measured between the normal and the reflected ray.
4. Ray paths are reversible. A ray travels back along the path it came.
5. Incoming parallel rays are reflected to a focus point.
6. Transmitted signals are reflected into a parallel beam from a focus point.

6. Describe satellite communication or tv link, repeaters and boosters using p 63.
7. Curved reflectors are used both for transmission and for reflection.
8. Total internal reflection occurs when light in a dense material (glass) meets a less dense material (air). If the angle of incidence is large, the ray is reflected and does not leave the material.
8. Critical angle is the angle the incident ray is at when the ray changes from refracting out to total internal reflection. At the critical angle the emerging ray is at 90°. (About 42° for normal glass.)
9. Electrical signals are changed to light. Light travels along an optical fibre by a series of total internal reflections. The light travelling along inside the narrow optical fibre always hits the glass boundary at a large angle, greater than the critical angle. The light is changed back to electrical signals.

Refraction: pp 66–69

1. What is refraction of light?
2. What way does light change direction from air to glass or glass to air?
3. What measurements are made when light is refracted?
4. What shapes are converging and diverging lenses?
5. What do lenses do to parallel rays of light?
6. Draw ray diagrams showing different uses of a converging lens.
7. What is the relationship between power and focal length?
8. What is the meaning of long and short sight? How do lenses correct long and short sight?

1. When light moves from one density of material into another there is a change in velocity and often a change in direction.
2. When light travels from air to glass it bends towards the normal. When light travels from glass to air it bends away from the normal. The angle is smallest in the glass.
3. The normal is a line at right angles to the surface. Angles are measured from the normal. The normal is 0°. The angle of incidence is measured between the normal and the incident ray. The angle of refraction is measured between the normal and the refracted ray.
4. Converging lenses are thicker in the middle. Diverging lenses are thickest at the sides.
5. A CONVERGING lens refracts light so that the rays converge to a focal point.
   A DIVERGING lens refracts light so that the rays diverge as if away from a focal point.

6. Use p 68 to show the object at more than two focal lengths from the lens, between one and two focal lengths from the lens and less than one focal length in front of the lens.
7. Power P is inversely proportional to focal length f in metres. Power is measured in dioptres D.
$$P = \frac{1}{f}$$
8. A long-sighted person sees distant objects clearly but not close-up. A converging lens will correct this. A short-sighted person sees close-up clearly only. A diverging lens will correct this.

Radioactivity

The atom and radioactivity

Everything is made of **atoms**. Elements have only one kind of atom but compounds have molecules made of two or more kinds of atoms. There are just over 100 kinds of atoms to make everything from.

Normally atoms are electrically **neutral**:
the number of positive protons = the number of negative electrons.

The atom has a **central positive nucleus** which is **tiny** but contains a lot of **mass**. **Electrons,** which are very small, **orbit** around the nucleus. Most of an atom is **empty space**.

the atom
nucleus
protons (+)
neutrons (0)

orbiting
electrons (–)

Properties of radioactivity

Some atoms have **unstable nuclei** and **emit particles** and **energy** to become more stable. They are radioactive atoms. The unstable nuclei **disintegrate** into different nuclei. **Alpha** and **beta** are particles. **Gamma** is energy.

Top Tip
Nuclear radiation:
Radiation comes from the nucleus of an atom.

α particles, β particles and γ-rays are all **nuclear radiations** as they are all emitted from the nucleus.

Type	Symbol	Nature	Mass (a.m.u.)	Charge	Speed	Absorbed
alpha particle	$^{4}_{2}\alpha$	2 neutrons + 2 protons	4	+2	$\leq 0.1c$	skin, paper or 3–5 cm air
beta particle	$^{0}_{-1}\beta$	fast electron	$\frac{1}{1840}$	-1	$\leq 0.9c$	3 cm tissue or 3 mm Al.
gamma ray	$_{-}\gamma$	High frequency energy wave	0 (waves have no mass)	0	c	3+ cm lead

(c = speed of light)

An **alpha particle** is **two protons and two neutrons** emitted from a large unstable nucleus. Alpha has **positive** charge.

A **beta particle** is a very fast **electron**. Beta particles are emitted from the nucleus when a neutron breaks up into a proton and the fast electron. Beta is a lot smaller than alpha and is **negative**.

Gamma rays are **energy waves** of very high frequency. A nucleus emits this energy to become more stable. Gamma rays have **no mass or charge**.

Absorption of radioactivity

Radiation energy may be **absorbed** in the medium through which it passes. The absorption properties can identify the type of radiation:

- A slow **alpha particle** cannot penetrate more than about **5 cm of air**. Alpha is easily stopped by a few **sheets of paper**. Alpha cannot penetrate your **skin**. (Swallowing alpha emitter is lethal as they don't escape.)

- Fast **beta particles** can penetrate through **several metres of air** before losing their energy. Beta particles are stopped by a **few millimetres of aluminium**.

- **Gamma rays** penetrate the **earth's atmosphere**. Air does not absorb gamma. They have very high energies. They can only be stopped by **several centimetres of lead** or **several metres of concrete**.

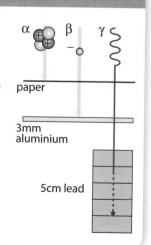

α β γ

paper

3mm aluminium

5cm lead

Ionisation

Atoms are normally electrically neutral.
Ionisation occurs when an atom **gains or loses** one or more **electrons**.

- Adding an electron to an atom creates a **negative ion** with more electrons than protons.
- Removing an electron from an atom creates a **positive ion** with less electrons than protons.

The nucleus and the number of protons remain unchanged during ionisation.

Ionisation can be caused by radioactivity. **Alpha α, beta β**, and **gamma γ** are **ionising radiations** as they can ionise atoms they hit. When ionising radiations collide with atoms they can knock an electron away leaving a positive ion.

Ionisation density is the amount of ionisation produced in a unit of volume.

Alpha particles produce a much greater ionisation density than beta particles or gamma rays.

Alpha particles cause the **most ionisation** because they are the **largest** and because they have the **greatest charge** of the radiations. Their **large mass** and **charge** make it easier to remove an electron from a neutral atom. As alpha particles cause the most ionisation they **give up their energy quickest** and are **absorbed in the shortest distance**.

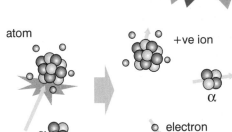

atom
+ve ion
α
electron

Ionisation technology smoke detector

Americium is a source of **alpha particles**. The ionisation chamber is two discs about 1 cm apart with a battery across. The alpha particles enter between the discs and cause **ionisation** of the air. The ions complete the electrical circuit and there is a **current**. In a fire, **smoke** enters the chamber and **neutralises the ions**. There is a **drop in the current** which is used to trigger the alarm.

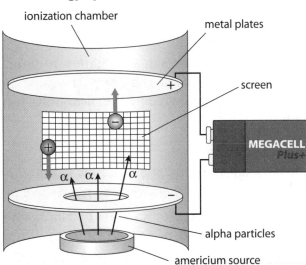

ionization chamber
metal plates
screen
MEGACELL Plus+
α α α
alpha particles
americium source

Quick Test

1. Why is an atom normally neutral?
2. Where are the protons in an atom?
3. Which radiation is not a particle?
4. What is the most penetrating radiation?
5. Which radiation causes the greatest ionisation?
6. What happens to radiation energy as it passes through a material?

Answers 1. No. of electrons = no. of protons **2.** Protons are in the nucleus. **3.** Gamma is not a particle. **4.** Gamma is the most penetrating radiation. **5.** Alpha causes the greatest ionisation. **6.** Radiation energy is absorbed as it passes through a material.

Uses of radiation

Detectors of radiation

The Geiger-Muller tube

A **Geiger-Muller (GM) tube** uses **ionisation** to detect alpha α, beta β, and gamma γ radioactivity. The tube is normally attached to a **counter** or **scaler** to record the activity.

Geiger-Muller tube   counter   front view

electrodes
gas
front view

The GM tube contains a **low pressure gas**. A **high voltage** is put across the **electrodes**. The **window** is made of **thin mica** that even **alpha can enter**. If any radiation enters the tube it causes **ionisation** in the **gas**. An electron moving towards the positive **electrode** causes **collisions** creating an **avalanche of electrons** which forms a pulse of electricity. This **pulse** is recorded as a **single count** on the counter.

Scintillation counters

Scintillation counters may be used to detect the various types of radioactivity (alpha α, beta β, and gamma γ), cosmic rays, and various other particles. Scintillations are **tiny flashes of light** emitted when a radiation strikes a **fluorescent substance**. The **radiation is absorbed** and its energy is **emitted** as **light**. The flashes can be seen by the eye or **amplified** and **counted** with **photo-multipliers** and **electronic circuits**.

Thin Al window   crystal   Photo-cathode   Photo-multiplier tube   High voltage supplier and analyzer

X-rays

signal   signal
Photo-multiplier tube
crystal

A **gamma camera** contains **scintillation counters**. Patients can be given **radionuclides** which emit **gamma rays** from **inside the body**. The gamma rays hit **crystals** in the camera which **scintillate**. These **flashes** are turned into **electrical pulses** and the camera produces **images** of the **organs** of the body.

Film badges

A **film badge** works by **photographic fogging**. It is worn by health workers and others who use radioactive materials.

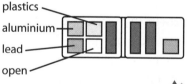

plastics
aluminium
lead
open

The **film** is in a **holder or badge**. The film is covered by **different types** and **thicknesses** of **absorber materials** such as **plastic, aluminium** and **lead**. After it has been worn, the film is developed. By examination, the **type** and **amount** of **exposure** can be seen. Film badges are used to detect **beta, gamma** and **X-rays**.

Top Tip
You must learn your choice of one of these detectors in detail.

Radiation and living cells

Radiation can **kill** living cells or **change the nature** of living cells.

The **energy** of the radiation can be **absorbed** and the radiation can cause **ionisation** of the atoms in the cell. This will **alter** the **cell properties**. For example, when radiation collides with a living cell, the **DNA** of the cell may alter. Radiation exposure may lead to **infertility** or **tumours**.

A large dose of radiation can kill a living cell.

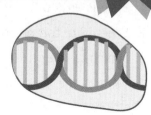

A cell and its DNA

Sterilisation and radiotherapy

Sterilisation

Radiation can kill cells. Radiation can be used in **sterilisation** to **kill bacteria** or germs.

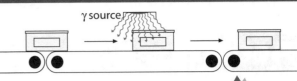

Medical instruments such as scalpels are **sterilised** by exposure to radiation. Syringes used to be made of glass and sterilised in boiling water or chemicals. Now cheap disposable plastic syringes are **irradiated** with a **strong gamma** source to kill bacteria so they won't cause infection. Irradiation with X-rays or gamma rays does **not** make materials radioactive.

Radiotherapy treatment

Radiation can kill cells. **Radiation therapy** (or **radiotherapy**) is the medical use of **ionising radiation** to control and **kill malignant cells**. Cancer cells stop reproducing, tumours shrink.

Top Tip
You have to learn one of these medical uses of radiation to destroy cells.

The radiation can be **high energy X-rays** or **gamma rays** from a radioactive source. Which beam is used depends on where the cancer is. These beams will have different energies and properties. They will penetrate to different depths.

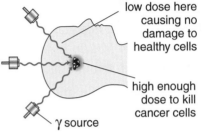

low dose here causing no damage to healthy cells

high enough dose to kill cancer cells

γ source

The radiations can be fired from **different positions** round the body so that the cancer cells get a strong dose yet the healthy tissue has a minimal dose. (A damaged healthy cell usually repairs itself.)

Radioactive tracers

In medicine

Radioactive tracers (a drug plus a gamma source) can be **injected** into the body and followed round the body as they **emit rays**. These rays are **easy to detect** outside the body. The tracer is **concentrated** in the organ being looked at. It **decays quickly** and emits γ-rays which **penetrate** through and **out** of the body. A **gamma camera** is positioned over the patient. Signals from the camera build up an **image** on a **monitor** screen.

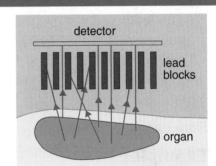

detector

lead blocks

organ

In agriculture

A **radioactive isotope** can be added to **fertilisers** to study how well plant nutrients are taken up by growing plants. Measuring how radioactive a plant has become indicates how well the fertiliser is working.

Top Tip
You have to learn one of these 'easy to detect' uses of radiation.

In industry

Radioactive tracers can be added to liquids to study their **flow** in **pipes** and **rivers**. The surrounding areas **can easily be monitored** for leaks.

Quick Test

1. Name three detectors of radiation.

2. Describe how one detector of radiation works.

3. What can radiation do to living cells?

4. List two medical uses of radiation to destroy cells.

5. List examples of radiation monitoring.

Answers 1. GM tube, scintillation counters, film badges **2.** See p.74. **3.** Cell death or cell alteration **4.** Instrument sterilisation, radiotherapy **5.** Tracers in medicine, agriculture and industry

75

Measuring radiation

Activity

Unstable nuclei of radioactive atoms disintegrate by giving out ionising radiations, e.g. alpha α, beta β, and gamma γ radiation. The nucleus is said to decay as it has now become a different nucleus. The atom is now a different atom.

CAUTION

RADIOACTIVE MATERIALS

The **activity** of a radioactive source is the **number of decays per second**.

The activity (A) of a radioactive source is measured in **becquerels (Bq)**.

Activity = $\dfrac{\text{Number of decays}}{\text{time}}$	$A = \dfrac{N}{t}$

N is just the number of nuclei that decay and has no units
t is the time in seconds
then activity A is measured in Bq.

One becquerel is equal to one disintegration or **one decay per second**. An activity of 500 Bq means that 500 nuclei are breaking up every second and 500 radiations are being emitted every second from these nuclei.

The units kBq, MBq and GBq are also common. (k = kilo = 1000, M = Mega = 1 000 000, G = Giga = 1 × 10⁹)

Top Tip
1 Bq is a very small unit of activity.

Antoine Henri Becquerel shared the 1903 Nobel Prize in physics with **Marie** and **Pierre Curie** for their work on radioactivity.

The value of **activity varies** with the **material** and the amount of **mass**:

Source	Activity (Bq)
1 litre seawater	10
1 g uranium 235	77 700
1 g plutonium 239	2.3×10^9
1 g radium 226	3.7×10^{10}

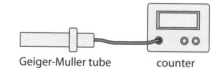

Geiger-Muller tube   counter

What is the activity of 1 kg of radium?

Since there are 1000 g in a kg, $1000 \times 3.7 \times 10^{10} = 3.7 \times 10^{13}$ Bq

Examples

What is the activity of a radioactive source if the number of nuclei in the source decaying every minute is 90 000.

$$A = \frac{N}{t} = \frac{90\,000}{60} = 1500 \text{ Bq}$$

A radioactive source emitting alpha particles has an activity of 1200 Bq. How many nuclei have disintegrated in 3 minutes?

$$N = At = 1200 \times (3 \times 60) = 216\,000$$

(Note there are no units for the number.)

How long does it take for 1 million nuclei to disintegrate from 1 g of radium 226?

$$t = \frac{N}{A} = \frac{1 \times 10^6}{3.7 \times 10^{10}} = 3 \times 10^{-5} \text{ s}$$

The activity of a radioactive source decays with time. (See Half-life, p 80.)

Absorbed dose

The **energy** of radiation may be **absorbed** in the medium through which it passes.
A body has most damage when a lot of energy is absorbed in a small amount of mass.

The **absorbed dose D** is the **energy absorbed per unit mass** of the absorbing material.

$$\text{Dose} = \frac{\text{Energy}}{\text{mass}}$$

$$D = \frac{E}{m}$$

Energy is measured in joules J.
Mass is measured in kilograms kg.
The gray Gy is the unit of absorbed dose.

$$1 \text{ Gy} = 1 \text{ J/kg}$$

When ionising radiation is used to treat cancer, the doctor will usually prescribe
the radiotherapy treatment in Gy.

Example

A radiation worker of mass 80 kg absorbs 0.16 J
of energy across his body. Calculate the absorbed dose.

$$D = \frac{E}{m} = \frac{0.16}{80} = 0.002 \text{ Gy} = 2 \text{ mGy}$$

Equivalent dose

The study of radiation victims has indicated that a dosage of alpha particles causes
much more harm than the same dosage from gamma rays. Alpha has a high ionisation
density. A **radiation weighting factor** w_R is given to **each kind of radiation** as a
measure of its **biological effect**.

Radiations	Weighting factor w_R
beta β, gamma γ and X-rays	1
slow neutrons	3
protons p and fast neutrons n	10
alpha α	20

Top Tip
Weighting factor is just a multiplier.

The **equivalent dose H** is the **product** of **absorbed dose D** and **radiation
weighting factor** w_R.

$$H = D\, w_R$$

Equivalent dose H is measured in **sieverts Sv**

Example

A radiation worker receives two types of exposure during a year, 150 μGy from fast neutrons and
2 mGy from alpha particles. Calculate the equivalent dose in total for the year.

Fast neutrons: $H = D\, w_R = 0.000150 \times 10 = 0.0015 \text{ Sv}$
Alpha particles: $H = D\, w_R = 0.002 \times 20 = 0.04 \text{ Sv}$
Total equivalent dose received by this worker in one year = 0.0415 Sv = 41.5 mSv

Quick Test

1. Calculate the activity of radiation when 6 million counts are recorded in 5 minutes.

2. What is the dose when 0.2 J is absorbed by 5 kg of tissue?

3. A patient has a CT scan. The absorbed dose is 0.04 Gy on 3 kg of the body. How much energy is received?

4. Alpha particles give a hospital worker an absorbed dose of 5 μGy. What is the equivalent dose?

Answers 1. $A = N/t = 6 \times 10^6 / (5 \times 60) = 2 \times 10^4$ Bq **2.** $D = E/m = 0.2 / 5 = 0.04$ Gy **3.** $E = Dm = 0.04 \times 3 = 0.12$ J **4.** $H = D\, w_R = 5 \times 10^{-6} \times 20 = 100 \times 10^{-6} = 100$ μSv

Biological harm and background radiation

Biological harm

The **equivalent dose H** takes into account:

- the **size** of the dose and
- the **type** of radiation

The potential damage from the source of radiation can then be compared.

The equivalent dose does **not** take into account the **type of material or tissue** the radiation falls on.

The amount of **biological harm** from exposure to radiation depends on both the source of radiation and the type of tissue that absorbs the radiation. The risk to health depends on the **three factors**

- the **size** of the **absorbed dose D**
- the **kind** of **radiation** α, β, γ, **n** (and its weighting factor w_R)
- the **body organs or tissue** exposed

> **Top Tip**
> The final risk to health is often called the **EFFECTIVE EQUIVALENT DOSE.**

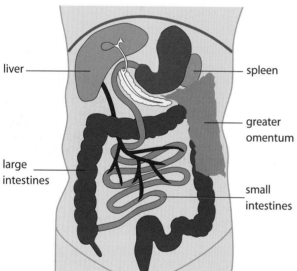

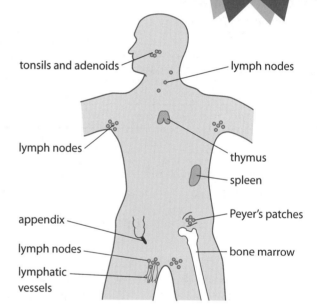

Organs and tissues of the body are illustrated but do not need to be learned.

As each organ or tissue type will respond in a different way to the radiation, the medical profession will factor this into their calculations before treating a patient.

Normally the equivalent dose of radiation from X-rays or CAT scans would be no more than a few mSv. Up to 100 mSv might be considered not to give any seen health effects.
A few sieverts Sv could cause burns or cancer or have other serious effect.
In treating tumours doctors will give high total dosage but spread the treatment over several weeks rather than give it in a short period. This is safer.
There is no totally safe level of ionising radiation. Physicists help to measure the radiation and calculate the risks of any treatment.

> **Top Tip**
> Learn the difference between absorbed dose, equivalent dose and effective equivalent dose.

Background radiation

Radiation is all around us. Everybody is exposed to this background radiation. It is around us all the time.

Geiger-Muller tube   counter

A Geiger-Muller tube and counter can be used to detect this background radiation.
A typical recording would be 30 counts entering the tube in a minute.
This is equal to an activity of 0.5 Bq.

Top Tip
Note the total equivalent dose from background radiation is about 2 mSv.

Background radiation comes from two types of source: natural and man-made:

NATURAL SOURCE	ANNUAL EQUIVALENT DOSE	
	µSv	mSv
Radioactive gases in air and buildings (radon and thoron)	800	0.8
Rocks of the earth	400	0.4
In food and our body	370	0.37
Cosmic rays from space	300	0.3
TOTAL NATURAL SOURCES	1870	1.87

MAN-MADE SOURCE	ANNUAL EQUIVALENT DOSE	
	µSv	mSv
Medical uses (X-rays)	250	0.25
Weapons testing	10	0.01
Nuclear industry (waste)	2	0.002
Other (Job, TV, flights)	18	0.018
TOTAL MAN-MADE SOURCES	280	0.28

Background radiation is mainly (nearly 90%) from natural sources.
Man-made exposure is mainly from medical uses.

The amount of exposure does vary with where you live and the job you do.

Radioactive gases

Radon Gas comes from rocks and spreads into the air. It can be trapped in poorly ventilated buildings.

Rocks

Rocks such as granite are high in radioactivity.

- Rad Gas
- Rocks
- Body, food
- Cosmic
- Medical
- Rest

Our Body

Our body contains potassium 40 which is radioactive. Food is slightly radioactive from the soil it is grown in.

Cosmic Rays

Radiation from the sun and outer space. The atmosphere absorbs most of this but this dose increases when flying.

Medical

X-rays, scans and cancer treatments from hospital.
A dental X-ray does negligible damage and reveals hidden problems.

Quick Test

1. What factors affect the biological harm done to a body?

2. Do man-made or natural sources contribute most to background radiation?

3. List the factors contributing to background radiation.

4. What is the typical equivalent dose per year for a person?

Answers 1. Dose, type and tissue 2. Natural 3. See p 79 4. 2 mSv

Half-life

Activity and half-life

When a radioactive source emits ionising radiations (alpha α, beta β, and gamma γ) its nuclei are disintegrating or 'decaying' and the source is changing into a different substance.

The activity depends on the number of nuclei in the source. If the size of a source is doubled, the activity will double.

The **activity** is the **number of disintegrations** occurring **per second**.

The activity of a radioactive source decreases with time.

As the nuclei disintegrate, there are fewer nuclei left to emit radiations. The **time taken** for **half the nuclei** in a radioactive substance to **decay** does not change. This time is the **half-life**.

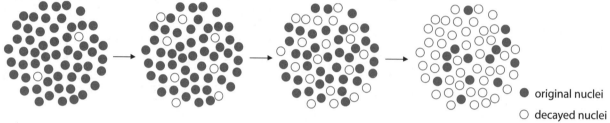

● original nuclei

○ decayed nuclei

The half-life of a radioactive substance is the time taken for the activity to drop to half its original value.

Radioactivity is a **random** process. The decay of an individual nucleus cannot be predicted. The decay in activity can only be predicted as there are large numbers of nuclei in any sample.

Nuclear Medicine	Sodium 24	15 hours
	Iodine 131	8 days
	Cobalt 60	5.3 years
Carbon Dating	Carbon 14	5760 years
Ageing Rocks	Uranium 238	4500 million years

Different substances have different half-life times:

Measuring half-life

To measure the half-life of a source we need:

- A **detector** of radiation, e.g. a Geiger-Muller tube and counter
- A **stopwatch**

First record the **background count** several times. Calculate the average and subtract this value from all readings.

Place the **source** a fixed distance in front of the Geiger counter and **record the count rate** at **regular time** intervals.

Plot the **count rate** (corrected for background count) against the **time taken** on a **graph**.

Measure the **time taken** from any **initial value** of count rate on the graph **to half this value**. The time for the count rate to keep halving stays the same. This is the **half-life time**.

Top Tip

You can read graph from any count rate that is easy to half to find half-life.

Count rate (counts/minute)

Geiger-Muller tube   counter

stopwatch

0   time

$t\frac{1}{2}$ $t\frac{1}{2}$ $t\frac{1}{2}$ $t\frac{1}{2}$

Calculations

The **fractional activity** is useful in understanding how the **activity changes with time**.

Remember a half-life has not taken place **until** the activity has halved.

Top Tip
Most half-life questions are one of these three types. Study well.

Number of half-lives	Activity (fraction)
Start = 0	1
1	1/2
2	1/4
3	1/8
4	1/16

Example 1

Calculate the half-life of the source whose activity has been recorded in the following table. The background count was recorded at 30 counts / minute.

Time (minutes)	0	30	60	90	120	150
Count rate (c/m)	834	580	429	288	232	175
Corrected count rate (c/m)	*804*	*550*	*399*	*258*	*202*	*145*

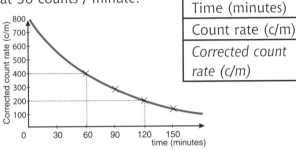

From the graph the half-life of this source is 60 minutes.

Example 2

A source of activity 12 000 kBq has a half-life of 4 weeks. It is locked in a cupboard for 16 weeks. What is its activity after this time?

Number of half-lives = $\dfrac{16}{4}$ = 4

$$12\,000 \;\rightarrow\; 6000 \;\rightarrow\; 3000 \;\rightarrow\; 1500 \;\rightarrow\; 750 \qquad \text{(or)}$$
$$\quad\;\; 1 \qquad\quad\; 2 \qquad\quad\; 3 \qquad\quad\; 4$$

The activity after 16 weeks is 750 kBq.

Activity	Number of half-lives
12 000	0
6000	1
3000	2
1500	3
750	4

Example 3

The activity of a radioactive source is 1600 MBq. 120 minutes later its activity is only 100 MBq. What is the half-life of the source?

$$1600 \;\rightarrow\; 800 \;\rightarrow\; 400 \;\rightarrow\; 200 \;\rightarrow\; 100 \qquad \text{(or)}$$
$$\quad\; 1 \qquad\quad 2 \qquad\quad 3 \qquad\quad 4$$

There are 4 half-lives.

The half-lives = $\dfrac{120}{4}$ = 30 minutes.

Activity	Number of half-lives
1600	0
800	1
400	2
200	3
100	4

Quick Test

1. What is half-life?
2. What is needed to measure half-life?
3. Activity drops from 1200 Bq to 300 Bq in 30 minutes. What is the half-life?
4. A source with activity 2400 Bq has a half-life of 5 s. What is the activity after 25 s?

Radiological protection

Safety procedures

The early discoverers of radioactivity were not aware of their **dangers**. We need to observe safe procedures.

The husband and wife team of **Marie** and **Pierre Curie** are credited with the discovery of **radioactive elements** in 1896–1900. They were researching in Paris. Henri Becquerel had **first discovered uranium rays** in 1896.

Marie invented the word **radioactivity** and discovered the radioactive elements polonium and radium.

Radioactive elements are **naturally occurring** and they can be used in science and medicine.

Radioactive elements can cause **major health problems** when they are present in high levels. Too much radiation causes tissue damage, cancer, genetic disorders, and even death. Marie Curie actually died as a result of her research.

Safety precautions for radioactive sources:

- Always handle or lift a radioactive source with **forceps**. Never use bare hands.
- **Never point** radioactive sources at anyone.
- **Never** bring a source **close** to your body or **point** at your eyes.
- After experiments with radioactivity, **wash hands** before eating. (Especially with open sources and radioactive rocks.)
- **Store** radioactive substances in **lead-lined holders**.
- After use, return to suitable safe, **locked store**.
- **Don't** allow persons **under 16** to handle radioactive sources.
- Radioactive **hazard signs** must be displayed.
- An authorised person must keep **records** of all radioactive sources.

Top Tip
Learn the precautions and the factors that reduce exposure.

Reducing exposure

Exposure to radiation can be harmful. The **equivalent dose** is **reduced** by **shielding**, by **limiting the time of exposure** or by **increasing the distance** from a source:

1 **Shielding**: **Lead** and **concrete** are good **absorbers** of radiation. A radioactive source is often kept in small lead cases. A radiographer will wear a lead lined apron. Schools or hospitals will often keep their sources behind brick or concrete walls. A nuclear plant will make use of thick concrete round its reactor.

2 **Limiting exposure time:** Sources should be brought in and used in as short a **time** as possible.

3 **Increasing distance from source:** Radiation often **spreads out** like the rays of a light bulb. This means that their **intensity decreases** rapidly with **distance**. Use **tongs** to **increase the distance** when in use. Just putting a source on the other side of the room when awaiting use may dramatically reduce exposure.

Radiation exposure is never reduced to zero. Background radiation is always present from the rocks, the soil and the air. In addition medical workers, dentists, research students, airline pilots, physics teachers and nuclear power workers accept a higher level of exposure as part of their job. Measurement and calculations are made and exposure is kept as low as possible using these reduction methods.

Hazard warning signs!

The **international radioactivity symbol** (known as trefoil).

This symbol is used to **identify materials** which are **radioactive**.

This symbol is used where radioactive materials are being **used** and where radioactive materials are being **stored**.

Top Tip
Look for these symbols in schools and hospitals.

Since 2007, this new symbol has been introduced to supplement the traditional symbol. The new symbol is to **alert** anyone, anywhere to the potential dangers of being **close** to a large source of ionising radiation.

Quick Test

1. Name several precautions you would take when handling radioactive substances.

2. State the three ways of reducing the equivalent dose of radiations.

3. State two places you would see the radioactive hazard sign.

Answers 1. See list p 82 **2.** Shielding, limiting time, increasing distance **3.** On radioactive materials, where used, where stored.

Nuclear power and reactors

Nuclear power and reactors

Electrical energy is one of the most **convenient** forms of energy. It is easily converted into other forms of energy that we need. Electrical energy is produced in **power stations**. **Nuclear fuel** is one of the sources that can be used to produce electrical energy by a power station.

Advantages of nuclear power

- Nuclear power stations **do not produce greenhouse effect gases**, thermal power stations do.
- Nuclear power does **not need fossil fuels**, which are in short supply.
- Nuclear power produces **huge amounts of energy** from very **small** amounts of fuel.
- Nuclear power stations produce **small** amounts of **waste**.
- Nuclear power is **very reliable**. Renewable sources depend on the wind and the sun.

Disadvantages of nuclear power

- Nuclear power stations produce dangerous, **radioactive** waste. This waste has to be stored for a **very long time**. This is the main disadvantage.
- Uranium is a **non-renewable** fuel. Other fuel processes are possible though.
- There is a risk of **radioactive** material escaping from a nuclear power station in an accident.
- Nuclear power stations may be expensive to decommission when their useful life is over.

Radioactive waste is the biggest problem for nuclear power. There is **low** and **medium** level waste which can be treated in a similar way to dangerous waste from other industries. The **high** level waste is the more problematic. High level waste can **remain radioactive** for **thousands of years**. The waste is carefully packed and **stored** in **safe stable rock formations**. In future other ways of storing or using this fuel waste may be possible.

Top Tip
You should learn to describe the process of fission.

Nuclear fission

In a nuclear power station, a nuclear **reactor** is used to **produce heat**.

In the reactor, nuclear fuel (uranium) is bombarded with neutrons to induce nuclear fission.

The **uranium 235** nucleus **absorbs a neutron**, then the nucleus **splits** into **two fission fragments** plus two or **three neutrons** and a large amount of **energy** are also released. This energy drives the power station.

The process of **splitting** the nucleus is called nuclear **fission**.

A chain reaction

The neutrons released during fission can set off a **chain reaction**. Each **neutron** released can be made to cause a **further** fission reaction. The reaction multiplies. In a nuclear bomb the fuel will be mainly uranium 235. In a power station the fuel has only a little uranium 235 and also uses control rods to absorb neutrons.

Top Tip
You should learn to explain a chain reaction.

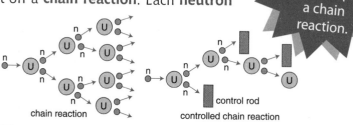

chain reaction

control rod

controlled chain reaction

Nuclear power stations

The main parts of a nuclear power station are a **nuclear reactor** followed by a **turbine** and **generator**. The nuclear reactor uses **fission** of a **fuel** such as **uranium** to produce large amounts of **heat** energy. The **heat** is used to make **steam** to drive the **turbine** and **generator**. **Nuclear fuel has been converted to electrical energy.**

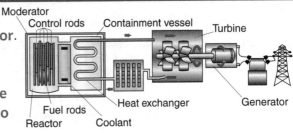

The turbine and generator will be similar to that found in a thermal (coal, oil or gas) power station.

Fuel rods

Pellets of fuel for fission are stacked in columns to make **fuel rods**. The fuel is often **enriched** uranium. This contains a higher percentage of the required uranium 235 than normal. The amount of uranium in a rod is small (well below critical mass) so it will never cause an explosion. The rods are in groups to form a fuel element.

Moderator

The neutrons emitted during fission are too fast. Fast neutrons are **moderated** (slowed) so that they can cause further fission. The fuel rods are placed in a moderator (**graphite**, water or heavy water). Neutrons from one fuel rod pass through the moderator and cause further fission in another rod.

Control rods

Electrical energy supply is maintained if one neutron from each fission reaction causes a further fission. This happens in a **controlled** chain reaction. **Control rods** made of **boron** can move in between the fuel rods to **absorb neutrons**. If electricity demand increases, the rods are raised. If less electricity is required, the rods are lowered. Extra boron control rods can be lowered into the reactor to stop the chain reaction in an emergency.

Top Tip
Learn to describe the operation of a nuclear reactor.

Coolant

The **heat** produced in a nuclear reactor is removed using a **coolant**. The coolant can be a pressurised **liquid or gas** (e.g. water or carbon dioxide gas). The coolant then transfers its heat to water flowing through a **heat exchanger**. This water changes to **steam** which can rotate the turbine.

Containment vessel

The core parts of a nuclear reactor are surrounded by a **containment vessel**. (A **steel** lining and several metres of **concrete**.) In the event of an accident the radiation including gamma rays and neutrons is **contained**. The containment vessel also protects the core from earthquakes and plane crashes.

Quick Test

1. List advantages and disadvantages of nuclear power.
2. What is nuclear fission?
3. Describe a fission reaction.
4. Name four parts of a nuclear reactor.
5. What is the problem with nuclear waste?

Answers 1. See p 84 **2.** Splitting of nucleus **3.** Neutron absorbed by nucleus which breaks into smaller parts and energy is released **4.** 4 of: fuel rods, moderator, control rods, coolant, containment vessel **5.** It is radioactive.

Key facts and questions

Summary questions and answers. Fuller answers are obtained by referring back to the revision notes.

Ionising radiations: pp 72–75

1. Describe a simple model of the atom.
2. What are alpha α, beta β, and gamma γ?
3. What happens to radiation in a medium?
4. What is the range and absorber of α, β and γ radiation?
5. Explain ionisation.
6. What radiation produces the greatest ionisation density?
7. Describe how one of the effects of radiation is used in a detector of radiation.
8. What can radiation do to living cells?
9. Describe one medical use of radiation which destroys cells.
10. Describe one use of radiation which shows it is easy to detect.

Answers

1. The atom has a central positive nucleus which is tiny but contains a lot of mass. The nucleus has protons (+) and neutrons (0). Electrons (−), which are very small, orbit around the nucleus. Most of an atom is empty space.
2. Alpha α, beta β, and gamma γ are ionising radiations from the nucleus. An alpha particle is made of two protons and two neutrons. A beta particle is a very fast electron. Gamma rays are short wave energy waves.
3. Radiation energy may be absorbed in the medium.
4. Alpha α: 5 cm air or sheet of paper. Beta β: several metres of air or 3 mm aluminium. Gamma γ: air does not absorb gamma. 5 cm lead.
5. Ionisation occurs when an atom gains or loses one or more electrons to become a negative or positive ion.
6. Alpha particles produce a much greater ionisation density than beta particles or gamma rays.
7. Describe one of Geiger counter, scintillation counters or film badges, p 74.
8. Radiation can kill living cells or change the nature of living cells.
9. Describe instrument sterilisation or radiotherapy treatment from p 75.
10. Describe one use of tracers in medicine, agriculture or industry from p 75.

Dosimetry: pp 76–79

1. What is meant by the activity of a radioactive source?
2. What is absorbed dose?
3. What is a radiation weighting factor?
4. What is equivalent dose?
5. What does the risk of biological harm from exposure to radiation depend on?
6. Describe factors affecting the background radiation.

Answers

1. The activity A of a radioactive source is the number of decays per second.

$$A = \frac{N}{t}$$

The activity of a radioactive source is measured in becquerels (Bq). One becquerel is one decay per second.

2. The absorbed dose D is the energy absorbed per unit mass of the absorbing material.

$$D = \frac{E}{m}$$

The gray Gy is the unit of absorbed dose. One gray Gy is equal to one joule per kilogram $1\,\text{Gy} = 1\,\text{J/kg}$

3. A radiation weighting factor w_R is given to each kind of radiation as a measure of its biological effect.
4. The equivalent dose H is the product of absorbed dose D and radiation weighting factor w_R.
   Equivalent dose H is measured in sieverts Sv $H = D\,w_R$
5. a. the absorbed dose D
   b. the kind of radiation, e.g. α, β, γ, n
   c. the body organs or tissue exposed
6. Describe radioactive gases in air, rocks, food & body, cosmic rays, medical uses, other p 79.

Half-life and safety: pp 80–83

1. What happens to the activity of a source?
2. What is the meaning of 'half-life'?
3. Describe how to measure half-life.
4. What fraction of activity is left after each of the first few half-lives? Start = 1.
5. What safety procedures are necessary when handling radioactive substances?
6. How is the equivalent dose reduced?
7. What is the radioactive hazard sign?

7.

1. The activity of a radioactive source decreases with time.
2. The half-life of a radioactive substance is the time taken for the activity to drop to half its original value.
3. A detector and a stopwatch are needed. Details on p 80.
4. $\frac{1}{2}$, $\frac{1}{4}$, $\frac{1}{8}$, $\frac{1}{16}$ … For more half-life calculation examples see p 81.
5. Monitor and keep records, use forceps, point away, wash hands, store in lead-lined boxes, lock store, display signs.
6. By shielding, by limiting the time of exposure or by increasing the distance from a source.

Nuclear reactors: pp 84–85

1. What are the advantages and disadvantages of nuclear power?
2. Describe the process of fission.
3. Explain a chain reaction.
4. Describe the principles of operation of a nuclear reactor.
5. Describe the problems with disposal and storage of radioactive waste.

Answers

1. Advantages of nuclear power
Nuclear power stations do not produce greenhouse effect gases, do not need fossil fuels, produce huge amounts of energy from very small amounts of fuel, produce small amounts of waste, are very reliable.

Disadvantages of nuclear power
Nuclear power stations produce dangerous, radioactive waste, which has to be stored for a very long time. Uranium is a non-renewable fuel. There is a small risk of radioactive material escaping from a nuclear power station in an accident. Nuclear power stations are expensive to decommission when their useful life is over.

2. The process of splitting the nucleus is called nuclear fission. The uranium-235 nucleus absorbs a neutron, then the nucleus splits into two fission fragments plus two or three neutrons and a large amount of energy is also released.
3. The two or three neutrons released during fission can set off a chain reaction. Each neutron released can be made to cause a further fission reaction.
4. Describe the fuel rods, moderator, control rods, coolant and containment vessel. See p 85.
5. High level waste can remain radioactive for thousands of years. The waste is carefully packed and stored in safe stable rock formations.

Formulae

Mechanics and heat

$$v = \frac{d}{t} \qquad d = vt \qquad v = \frac{s}{t} \qquad s = vt \qquad a = \frac{v - u}{t} \qquad F_{un} = ma \qquad W = mg$$

N1 An object will remain at rest or will remain at constant velocity unless acted on by an unbalanced force.

N2 The acceleration of an object varies directly with the unbalanced force and inversely with its mass.

N3 'If A exerts a force on B, then B exerts an equal but opposite force on A.'

$$p = mv \qquad \textbf{total } \text{momentum before} = \textbf{total } \text{momentum after} \qquad m_1u_1 + m_2u_2 = m_1v_1 + m_2v_2$$

$$E_W = Fd \qquad P = \frac{E_W}{t} \qquad E_P = mgh \qquad E_K = \frac{1}{2}mv^2$$

$$\text{Percentage Efficiency} = \frac{E_O}{E_i} \times 100 \qquad \text{Percentage Efficiency} = \frac{P_O}{P_i} \times 100$$

$$E = cm\Delta T \qquad E = ml \qquad (l_v \text{ or } l_f) \qquad v = \text{vapourisation} \qquad f = \text{fusion}$$

Electricity and electronics

$$I = \frac{Q}{t} \qquad Q = It \qquad R = \frac{V}{I} \qquad V = IR \qquad \frac{V_1}{V_2} = \frac{R_1}{R_2} \qquad V_2 = \frac{R_2}{R_1 + R_2} . V_s$$

Series: $\qquad I_S = I_1 = I_2 = I_3 \qquad V_S = V_1 + V_2 + V_3 \qquad R_T = R_1 + R_2 + R_3$

Parallel: $\qquad I_S = I_1 + I_2 + I_3 \qquad V_S = V_1 = V_2 = V_3 \qquad \frac{1}{R_T} = \frac{1}{R_1} + \frac{1}{R_2} + \frac{1}{R_3}$ $\qquad$ (s = supply)
(T = total)

$$P = \frac{E}{t} \qquad P = IV \qquad P = I^2R \qquad P = \frac{V^2}{R}$$

mains supply: $\qquad$ Frequency = 50 Hz $\qquad$ Quoted voltage = 230 V $\qquad$ Peak voltage ~ 325 V

transformer equations: $\qquad P_{in} = I_pV_p \qquad P_{out} = I_sV_s \qquad \frac{n_s}{n_p} = \frac{V_s}{V_p} + \frac{I_p}{I_s}$

$$\text{Voltage gain} = \frac{\text{Voltage Output}}{\text{Voltage Input}} \qquad \text{Gain} = \frac{V_{Out}}{V_{In}}$$

Waves and optics

$$d = vt \qquad v = f\lambda \qquad \text{frequency} = \frac{\text{number of waves}}{\text{time taken}} \qquad P = \frac{1}{f}$$

Radioactivity

$$A = \frac{N}{t} \qquad D = \frac{E}{m} \qquad H = D_{WR}$$

Guide

General guidance

Physics is a practical as well as a theoretical subject. Practical assessments will be part of your course. They may be undertaken as you go through the course, as the practical experiments for assessment are selected from the normal experiments that are part of the Intermediate 2 course. If you learn to describe the experiments properly, using the guide below, you may need to do fewer assessments to reach the required standard for submission.

There are different practical experiments that can be chosen from each unit. The experiment, however, has to be complex enough to allow all the required points to be assessed so not all experiments are suitable. The following pages show typical experiments and instructions.

There follows a quick guide to what to expect and some suggested experiments. Remember to write your report in the **impersonal passive voice** using the **past tense**. For example, 'The light gate was connected ...' not 'I connected the light gate ...' Keep sentences brief, clear and to the point.

In an experiment you will usually be altering an independent variable and measuring how this affects the dependent variable. These two variables will feature, for example, in the aim, procedure and conclusion. To be sure of making a fair test, other variables should not be altered throughout the experiment.

Top Tip
It is advisable to use the **report headings** when writing your assessment.

Report writing

- The guidance below can be altered to suit the experiment you are doing.

TITLE: From your **instruction** sheet. *Keep this simple.*

AIM or OBJECTIVE: State the purpose of the experiment. *This should not show the result you expect. You have to find how one variable changes as you change another.*

APPARATUS: List the apparatus and/or **draw** a labelled diagram. *You should receive help with this on the instruction sheet.*

PROCEDURE: How the **independent variable was altered** and how **measurements** were taken. *Remember there are two main variables here, the independent and the dependent variable. Describe what you are doing and how you are making the measurements.*

READINGS/RESULTS: A clear **table** or tables with quantities and units in the headings. Give repeated and averaged results where you can. A **graph** with labelled axis, plotted points and line or curve of **best fit**. *You will not usually be told to repeat your readings or to graph your results. You will not be given a blank table. However you will be*

told to 'use an appropriate format' and these may be what is required.

CONCLUSION: State any **pattern** to the results (graph) and **relation** between the **variables**. *It is your job to analyse any significnt trends in your results and say what you have found. Answer your aim.*

EVALUATION: How **effective** was the procedure? Could you get a conclusion from the results? Could you control the variables? Are there sources of error? Do you need to improve the apparatus? (At least one of these.) *If you get a good set of results you do not need to change all the apparatus! Evaluation can be positive as well as negative.*

Notes:

- Remember: as well as checking your written report, your teacher will be checking that you are actively collecting your practical information when doing your experimental work.

- If there is something wrong or omitted you do not have to re-do the whole experiment. You can be given the report back to be modified and resubmitted.

Mechanics and heat

Variation of instantaneous speed with time for an accelerating object

APPARATUS: Runway, vehicle with mask, light gate, electronic timer or computer, stop-clock.

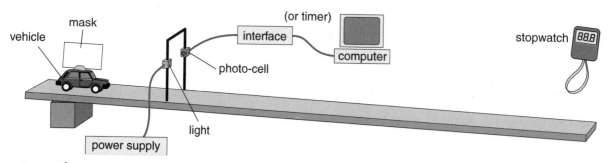

Instructions:

- Set the runway at a shallow angle so the vehicle will accelerate down the slope.
- Set the timer / computer to measure the instantaneous speed as the mask passes through the light gate.
- Release the vehicle from the top of the runway.
- Measure the time taken to reach the light gate.
- Record the speed of the vehicle through the light gate.
- Move the light gate further down the slope and repeat at least four more times.
- Use an appropriate format to show the variation of speed with time.
- **Complete your report.**

General:

You are recommended to use titles like those given in the preceeding guide. This will ensure you cover the requirements of the Intermediate 2 practical assessment. You should select or adapt the guidance to describe the experiment you are currently doing. An official advice to candidates sheet should be provided.

- **Title**
- **Aim** or **Objective**
- **Apparatus**
- **Procedure**
- **Readings / results**
- **Conclusion**
- **Evaluation**

Relationship between acceleration and applied force

APPARATUS: Linear air track and pulley, vehicle with double mask, light gate, electronic timer or computer, hanger and masses.

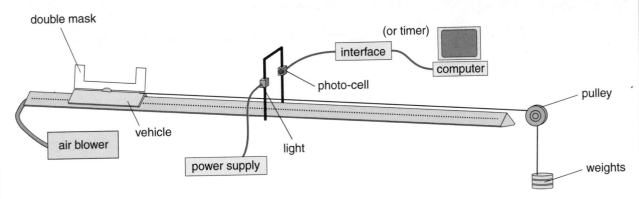

Instructions:

- Level the slope.
- Set the timer / computer to measure the acceleration as the mask passes through the light gate.
- Place only the hanger on the thread. Calculate its weight, this is the applied force.
- Place the other weights on the vehicle. The total mass of vehicle and weights will not change.
- Switch on the blower and measure the acceleration through the light gate.
- Move one weight off the vehicle and onto the hanger.
- Release the vehicle and record the new force and acceleration produced at least four more times.
- Use an appropriate format to show the variation of acceleration with the applied force.
- **Complete your report.**

General:

You are recommended to use titles like those given in the guide proceeding. This will ensure you cover the requirements of the Intermediate 2 practical assessment. You should select or adapt the guidance to describe the experiment you are currently doing. An official advice to candidates sheet should be provided.

- **Title**
- **Aim** or **Objective**
- **Apparatus**
- **Procedure**
- **Readings / results**
- **Conclusion**
- **Evaluation**

Electricity and electronics

Variation of current with potential difference for a given resistor

APPARATUS: Resistor, ammeter, voltmeter, variable power supply, connecting leads.

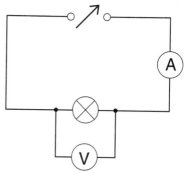

Instructions:

- Set up the circuit shown.
- Adjust the variable power supply to where it says 1 V. Switch on.
- Measure the current through the resistor and the potential difference across it.
- Adjust the supply in marked 1 V steps, repeating the measurements, to 5 V.
- Use an appropriate format to show the variation of current with potential difference.
- **Complete your report.**

General:

You are recommended to use titles like those given in the guide proceeding. This will ensure you cover the requirements of the Intermediate 2 practical assessment. You should select or adapt the guidance to describe the experiment you are currently doing. An official advice to candidates sheet should be provided.

- **Title**
- **Aim** or **Objective**
- **Apparatus**
- **Procedure**
- **Readings / results**
- **Conclusion**
- **Evaluation**

Variation of resistance with temperature for a thermistor

APPARATUS: Beaker of hot water, thermometer, ohmmeter, thermistor.

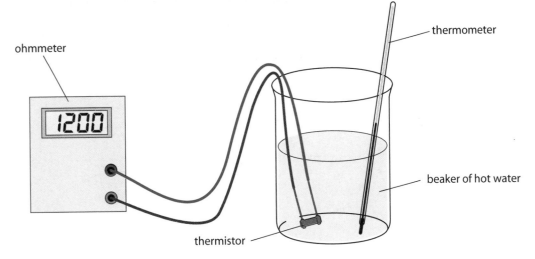

Instructions:

- Carefully pour hot water, about 80°C, into the beaker.
- Connect the thermistor to the ohmmeter.
- Place the thermistor into the water.
- As the water cools, record the resistance of the thermistor at regular intervals, e.g. 5°C.
- Stir the water gently between readings to obtain even temperature.
- Take at least five pairs of readings.
- Use an appropriate format to show the variation of resistance of a thermistor with temperature.
- **Complete your report.**

General:

You are recommended to use titles like those given in the guide proceeding. This will ensure you cover the requirements of the Intermediate 2 practical assessment. You should select or adapt the guidance to describe the experiment you are currently doing. An official advice to candidates sheet should be provided.

- **Title**
- **Aim** or **Objective**
- **Apparatus**
- **Procedure**
- **Readings / results**
- **Conclusion**
- **Evaluation**

Waves and optics

Variation of angle of refraction with angle of incidence

APPARATUS: Semi-circular perspex block, ray-box and power supply, protractor

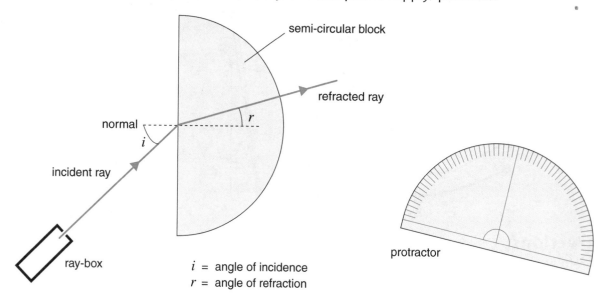

i = angle of incidence
r = angle of refraction

Instructions:

- Set up the apparatus as shown. Draw round the block.
- Mark the normal and at least five different angles of incidence (e.g. at 10° intervals).
- Record the angles of incidence and record and measure the corresponding angles of refraction.
- Use an appropriate format to show the variation of angle of refraction with angle of incidence.
- **Complete your report.**
- Note: you may wish to include your labelled experiment sheet showing your ray diagrams in your report.

General:

You are recommended to use titles like those given in the guide proceeding. This will ensure you cover the requirements of the Intermediate 2 practical assessment. You should select or adapt the guidance to describe the experiment you are currently doing. An official advice to candidates sheet should be provided.

- **Title**
- **Aim** or **Objective**
- **Apparatus**
- **Procedure**
- **Readings / results**
- **Conclusion**
- **Evaluation**

Radioactivity

Variation of the count rate of a beta source with thickness of absorber

APPARATUS: Radioactive source, Geiger-Muller tube and counter, aluminium sheets.

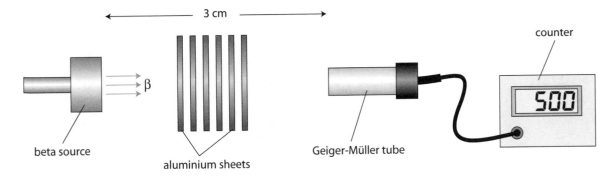

beta source
aluminium sheets
Geiger-Müller tube
counter

Instructions:

- Record the background count over a minute to subtract from future readings. Repeat and average.
- With the source 3 cm from the g-m tube, record the count over a minute.
- Insert a sheet of aluminium absorber, record the thickness and measure the new count rate.
- The aluminium sheets should be of known (e.g. 0.5 mm) or measured thickness.
- Repeat, adding absorber sheets at least four more times. Record the new measurements.
- Use an appropriate format to show the relationship between thickness and count rate from the source.
- **Complete your report.**
- Note: for safety reasons radioactivity experiments may be carried out as a teacher demonstration or shown as a video. You can record data and write your report from this.

General:

You are recommended to use titles like those given in the guide proceeding. This will ensure you cover the requirements of the Intermediate 2 practical assessment. You should select or adapt the guidance to describe the experiment you are currently doing. An official advice to candidates sheet should be provided.

- **Title**
- **Aim** or **Objective**
- **Apparatus**
- **Procedure**
- **Readings / results**
- **Conclusion**
- **Evaluation**

Intermediate 2 Physics
Index